A LABORATORY MANUAL

Experience The Extraordinary Chemistry of Ordinary Things

B. COBURN RICHARDSON
Highline Community College
Des Moines, Washington

THOMAS G. CHASTEEN
Sam Houston State University
Huntsville, Texas

JOHN WILEY & SONS, INC.
NEW YORK · CHICHESTER · BRISBANE · TORONTO · SINGAPORE

ISBN 0-471-55856-7

Printed and bound by Malloy Lithographing, Inc.

10 9 8 7 6 5 4 3 2

Printed in the United States of America

ACKNOWLEDGMENTS

Teacher authors are always in great debt to the two "S's"—students and shoulders. For sixteen years, students in "Chemistry for Those Who Hate Chemistry" classes at Highline Community College have unwittingly served as guinea pigs for many of the experiments in this manual. Our students continue to teach us how to design and write experimental procedures for the nonscientist. It has been a long and humbling but rewarding challenge.

No writer ever works in an intellectual vacuum, and many ideas have come from standing on the shoulders of our contemporaries and of those who have gone before. Had we been born thousands of years ago, we might be excited with experiments demonstrating the wheel or fire. We would especially like to thank Rubin Battino, James P. Birk, Arlo D. Harris, Martin G. Ondrus, and Michael Sady (and their coauthors) for their excellent *Journal of Chemical Education* articles from which five of these labs were drawn. Thank goodness that chemistry is a cumulative science and that those that have gone before (even just before) leave recorded tracks.

Without encouragement and setting of deadlines, however, none of these labors would have come together (at least not in our lifetimes) unless someone like Joan Kalkut at John Wiley & Sons were there to guide this joint project to its completion. And for the understanding support of our wives, Sharon and Tamara, we bequeath anew all our good intentions for attentions unrequited and "necessities" undone.

We encourage and actively solicit feedback from all who use this manual, and welcome any and all comments.

Tom Chasteen
Department of Chemistry
Sam Houston State University
Huntsville, TX 71340-5900

Bruce Richardson
Highline Community College
P.O. Box 98000
Des Moines, WA 98198-9800

PREFACE

This preface explains why your chemistry course has a lab, and why the lab is structured in its particular way. In answer to the first question, we must hasten to emphasize that, unlike liberal arts subjects like philosophy, chemistry is strictly an *experimental* science. This is not to imply that chemical knowledge has always progressed and expanded in an orderly fashion based upon scientific observations and experiments. Much chemical "thought" 2000 or so years ago evolved from an "armchair philosophy" rather than from deduction based upon careful experimentation, with the result that untruths and misconceptions retarded progress towards a real understanding of the matter/energy make-up of our world and universe for many centuries. The most noted fallout from this was perhaps the impossible attempts of alchemists to transmute (change) lead into gold by chemical reactions.

It is thus primarily through experimentation—especially quantitative experimentation where not only what happens is noted, but also how much of what—that the laws and concepts of chemistry have been clarified. Since such experimentation forms the basis of all our chemical knowledge, no chemistry course can really convey what chemistry is all about unless we have the chance to try our own handiworks with some "live" molecules, however modest the effort. The lab is where the action is, and it is hoped that it can and will make chemistry come alive for you and perhaps be that one aspect of the course that may linger longest in your memory (favorably, we hope). Some of you will be able to get good results in lab and some will have difficulty, but whatever your success or lack of it, you will know more about that particular aspect of a chemist's life. The nature of your results will not affect your lab grade. Chemistry can, but need not be, traumatic, numbing and nerve-wracking—but it can also be fun.

Now what about the design of the lab? In spite of the fact that this will be the first (and perhaps the last) chemistry course you'll ever take, the lab procedures in large measure do not follow a set "cookbook" of steps that everyone follows to the same supposed inevitable end. The techniques themselves will be described in considerable detail and are illustrated with drawings of apparatus and equipment, but each person or group may well be working on a different sample. This approach will demand extra time and responsibility on both your and your lab instructor's part, but these authors are willing to wager that you will come to agree the effort is worth it.

The basic objectives which guided the form and selection of experiments are the following:

1. Relate chemistry to that part of the world that is meaningful and/or familiar.

2. Stress sample-from-home type experiments.

3. Guarantee reasonable chance of experimental success.

4. Provide challenging experiments.

5. Maximize quantitative types of investigations.

6. Make any computations required relatively simple to perform without knowledge of algebra.

7. Cover as wide a variety of topics and techniques as possible.

8. Use experiments that can be performed (at least the laboratory part) within two hours.

9. Avoid toxic chemicals or hazardous procedures wherever possible.

10. Permit checking accuracy of results wherever possible by providing known samples or other necessary information.

11. Give very detailed experimental procedures, allowing for a variety of student-chosen samples, which take into account probable lack of scientific backgrounds and experience.

12. Give historical backgrounds and explain rationale for procedural steps—give the "whys" as well as the "whats."

The experiments selected are covered in depth and some use procedures rather sophisticated at the beginning level—but nonetheless adaptable by most students.

We mentioned responsibilities; you must agree and be willing to fulfill two duties if we are to succeed. First, you must attend lab faithfully; or to put it more candidly, lab attendance is required.

Second, you will find that most of the experiments require you to bring your own sample from home. Sure, we could provide you and everyone else with identical samples to test with results almost guaranteed. But that is not the intent; you are given the opportunity to pick, within limits of the type of experiment, a sample of your choice. It is your decision, your opportunity, but also your responsibility to bring the sample that is specified at the beginning of each lab—so don't blow it. A "forgotten" sample necessary for an analysis may mean you cannot do the experiment.

We now welcome you to our chemical lair—and the chance to enjoy some "Close encounters of the Chemical Kind." Don't forget your goggles....

Bruce Richardson
Red Chasteen
December 1992

CONTENTS

Experience The Extraordinary Chemistry of Ordinary Things

First Day in the Laboratory
or
(How I Survived in the Laboratory by Not Blowing Myself Up)

Check In

Check your drawer equipment against the supplied check sheet. Note any missing, broken or dirty equipment and get replacements from the stockroom.

Discussion

SURVIVING IN THE LAB BY NOT BLOWING YOURSELF UP
Laboratory Safety and Techniques Check List

We don't want to put the fear of chemistry in you (anymore than it may already be) by dwelling on the unpleasant, but as a metric equivalent of an English saying might go, "Thirty grams of prevention is worth 0.454 kilograms of cure." Working in the chemistry lab may actually be safer than working at home. Many of you have chemicals in your kitchen potentially more hazardous than anything you can probably see in a chemistry lab; for example, the aerosol can of oven cleaner containing potassium hydroxide!

1. Eye protection will be mandatory for most (if not all) experiments. This means that you must wear approved safety glasses or safety goggles.

2. If you spill a chemical on your skin or clothing, wash it immediately with plenty of water and consult your lab instructor. For the eyes, speed of washing is of utmost importance. Familiarize yourself with the location of the eye wash fountain and the use of sodium bicarbonate and acetic acid solutions.

3. If diluting sulfuric acid, pour the acid slowly into the water, stirring constantly. Never add the water to the acid, since so much heat is liberated that steam may be formed with almost explosive violence.

4. <u>NEVER</u> taste a chemical or solution unless directed to do so. Poisonous substances are not always so labeled in the laboratory.

5. When smelling the odor of a liquid, do not hold your face directly over the container, lest you chance an unpleasant surprise. Instead, fan a little of the vapor toward you by sweeping your hand over the top of the container towards your nose.

6. To protect your clothing from corrosive chemicals, an inexpensive plastic apron (much cheaper than new clothing) is strongly recommended.

7. When putting glass tubing through a rubber stopper, first put a drop of water or glycerine on the tubing and on the hole in the stopper. Hold the tubing with a cloth near the end to be inserted and insert with a twisting motion. <u>Don't force</u>. Accidents of this kind are the most common way hands become cut or impaled.

8. Do not point your test tube at your neighbor or yourself when heating substances. Sudden boiling may turn your test tube into a scalding liquid cannon!

9. Note the location of fire extinguishers, safety shower, fire blanket, and eye wash fountain and know how to use them.

Techniques

1. Put all solids to be discarded in the waste receptacles. Put wastepaper in the large wastebaskets for that purpose. Never throw matches, filter paper or any solid into the sink. Empty liquids into the sink along with plenty of running water unless directed otherwise by your lab instructor.

2. Avoid laying the stopper of a bottle down. Instead, pull it out by placing the back of your hand over the stopper and grasping it between the middle and forefinger. This same hand is now used to pick up the bottle as well; ignoring this technique could lead to contamination of the bottle contents.

3. Do not insert your own pipettes or medicine droppers into the regent bottles, but pour out a <u>little</u> of the solution into a small beaker for your own use. This will also avoid contamination.

4. Never return unused chemicals to the stock bottles. You may make a mistake from which another student's experiment will suffer. If you take too much of a chemical, either share with others or discard what is left over into an appropriate container labelled for that purpose.

5. Weigh solids on paper or a watch glass. Do not allow chemicals to come into contact with the balance pans to avoid contamination and corrosion.

6. Keep your working area orderly and leave it clean for the next person at all times.

7. Be forewarned that, however clean looking, bench tops may have chemical residues lurking on them and these residues may be ready to eat anything they come in contact with such as clothes, book bags, etc.

Safety Symbols

The experimental procedures that appear in this manual will be accompanied by safety symbols integrated into the text. These symbols are included to alert you, the experimenter, to that part of the procedure that requires extra care and attention. The specific safety symbols refer to specific dangers that may be encountered. For instance, the corrosive safety symbol will appear near the point in the procedure in which you are directed to use a strong acid or base or other corrosive material that requires care in handling.

The safety symbols that are used in this manual are listed below.

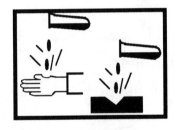

Corrosive Material

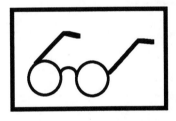

Eye Protection Required

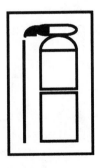

Fire Hazard

Poisonous Material

Common Laboratory Equipment

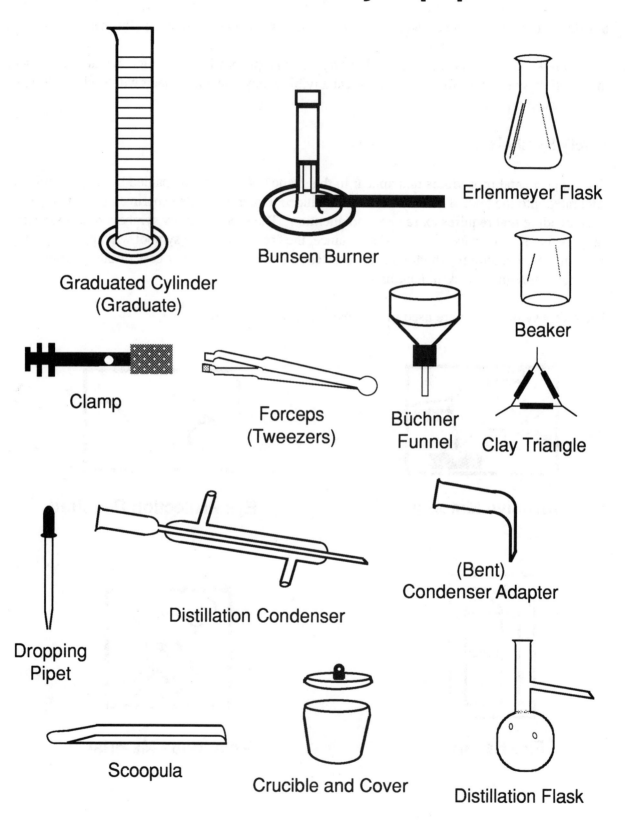

Graduated Cylinder
(Graduate)

Bunsen Burner

Erlenmeyer Flask

Beaker

Clamp

Forceps
(Tweezers)

Büchner
Funnel

Clay Triangle

Dropping
Pipet

Distillation Condenser

(Bent)
Condenser Adapter

Scoopula

Crucible and Cover

Distillation Flask

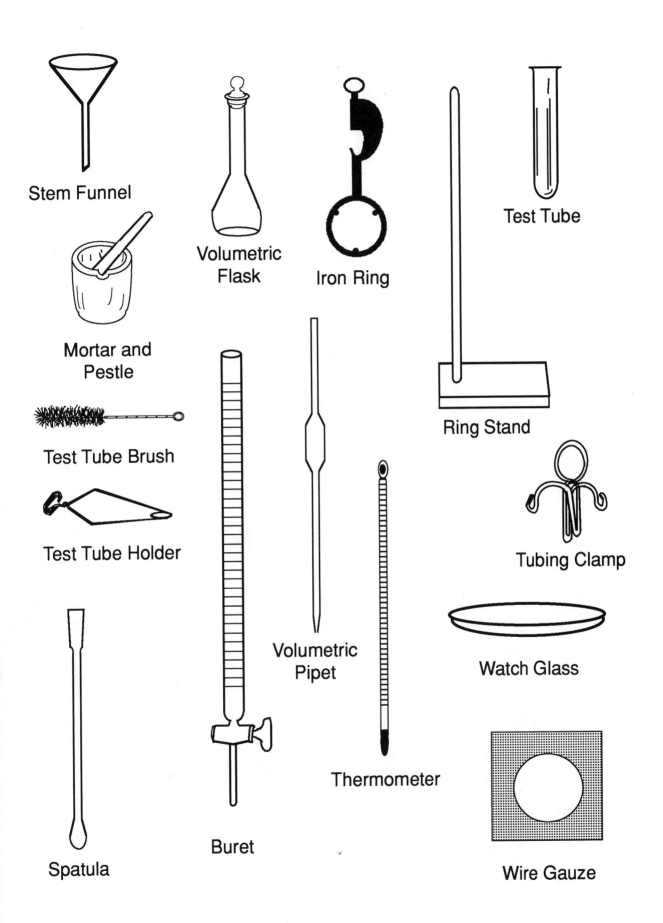

Stem Funnel

Mortar and Pestle

Test Tube Brush

Test Tube Holder

Spatula

Volumetric Flask

Iron Ring

Buret

Volumetric Pipet

Thermometer

Test Tube

Ring Stand

Tubing Clamp

Watch Glass

Wire Gauze

Experiment

1

The Ubiquitous Bunsen Burner

Sample From Home

No samples from home are needed for this experiment.

Objectives

You will examine the structure and function of the Bunsen burner and the effects that the air and gas flow controls have upon the color and hotness of the flame. Time and materials will also be available for experimenting with glassworking.

Background

Those pieces of laboratory equipment that visions of the proverbial white-smocked, bespectacled chemist conjures up in most people's mind would have to be the test tube—and the Bunsen burner. What self—respecting chemist indeed would be caught in any Hollywood movie without them! Although the Bunsen burner has been around ever since Robert Bunsen developed it back in 1855, it is still a workhorse in the lab for many heating jobs that do not require careful heat control, nor involve flammable chemicals.

Burning is a chemical process and involves a chemical reaction whereby a substance most commonly combines with oxygen in the air to produce new substances. These new substances, while containing all of the same original atoms, have entirely new physical and chemical properties. None of the atoms representing elements have changed their fundamental identity, but they have undergone a chemical change which is accompanied by drastic alterations in their properties. Thus the paraffin wax in a candle "burns" (reacts with oxygen) to produce carbon dioxide gas, water, light, and heat energy. Decaying organic matter such as leaves and humus also "burn", only not usually so fast that the heat is sufficient to cause ignition. Iron, too, slowly "burns" in air to produce rust—a new chemical compound of iron combined with oxygen.

The actual substance burned in the Bunsen burner is principally a gaseous paraffin hydrocarbon called methane (marsh gas or natural gas). A chemically correct equation for this reaction would read: methane and oxygen in air react to produce carbon dioxide, water, and energy. In chemist's formula notation, this would become

$$CH_4 + 2O_2 \xrightarrow{\Delta} CO_2 + 2H_2O + energy + h\sqrt{}$$

(1 molecule) + (2 molecules) ---->   (1 molecule) + (2 molecules)   +   (heat)   +   (light)
   methane   oxygen   carbon dioxide   water

The actual design of the Bunsen burner is in principle the same as for other types of gas flames, whether in a home gas stove or a welding torch. The purpose of this design is to premix the gas and oxygen (air) before ignition. This permits the combustion process to be more efficient, thereby producing more heat as well as a particular "hot zone" defined by the shape of the burner mouth. The flame color is an indication of how complete the burning has been. A yellow color in the flame is due to microscopic incandescent carbon particles ("soot"); this condition is undesirable because any carbon atoms escaping as such soot and not ending up in carbon dioxide reduce the efficiency and hence heat of the flame. But these are things you are to observe and verify in this experiment.

Procedure

1. Determine where the gas control is for your particular type of burner. Some may have a thumbscrew control underneath the base, but in any case the gas flow can always be adjusted back at the main valve at your desk station. The air control consists of vents at the base of the tall cylindrical chimney and can be opened and closed either with a circular slip-ring or by rotating the chimney itself. Turn on the gas and light the Bunsen burner. If the flame keeps blowing itself out, cut back a bit on the gas flow valve.

2. Shut off the air vents. In many burners this can only be done completely by tightly griping the bottom of the chimney and wrapping your hand around it. Yes, it is safe to carefully handle the Bunsen burner while it is lit. You MUST shut off the air vents to obtain valid observations. Any blueness to your flame means that you have not completely shut off the air.

(a) You should now have seen a dramatic change in the nature of the flame. Note the color and shape of your flame on the report sheet.

(b) Briefly (20-30 seconds) using your tongs, hold an evaporating dish (white porcelain) filled with cold water over this flame and observe any deposit formed on the underside of the dish.

(c) Hold your wire gauze for about 10 seconds at various levels in the flame in a horizontal position and pass it up and down through the flame. Does the wire glow red hot at any location in the flame? (If the gauze has white ceramic center, use the bare metal at the corners)

3. Now completely open the air vents. If your flame goes out, you may have to cut back slightly on the gas flow and relight the burner.

(a) You should now be able to discern a relatively colorless flame with two distinct conical sections. If in doubt, ask for help from your lab instructor.

(b) Repeat the test with your evaporating dish as in **2(b)**.

(c) Check the hotness (temperature) of your flame as in **2(c)**.

(d) Draw a temperature profile sketch, showing the general form of the flame and its coldest and hottest parts.

4. (*Optional*). Your instructor can demonstrate how to seal the end of glass tubing and then blow out (not blow up) sections of this glass. Help yourself to as many pieces of glass tubing as you can use and try your hand at some glassworking. Feel free to take home whatever you blow, bend, or stick together. EYE PROTECTION IS MANDATORY WHEN DOING ANY GLASS-BLOWING. If you wish to make colored glass, consult with your instructor on suitable methods.

Report Sheet—Experiment 1
The Bunsen Burner

Date _____   **Section number** _____   **Name** _____

1. Gas control located _____.

   Air control located _____.

2. Air vents closed

   (a) Appearance of flame _____.

   (b) Nature of deposit, if any, on dish (identify) _____.

   (c) Did your gauze glow red anywhere in flame? _____.

3. Air vents open

   (a) Appearance of flame _____.

   (b) Nature of deposit, if any, on dish _____.

   (c) Did your gauze glow red anywhere in flame? _____.

   (d) Draw the shape and temperature profile sketch of your flame below.

Questions—Experiment 1
The Bunsen Burner

Date _____ **Section number** _____ **Name** _____

1. Does soot represent an element or a compound? Explain.

2. Where do the carbon atoms come from in this experiment that are found in soot?

3. What percent or fraction of air is pure oxygen? What comprises most of the rest?

4. Why does mixing air in with gas before ignition give a hotter flame?

5. In glassblowing, the flame temperatures must be even hotter than those that can be obtained with your burner. Using the same fuel (methane), suggest how hotter flame temperatures are reached.

6. Have you read over the safety and technique procedures, and do you agree to try your best to follow them?

Think, Speculate, Reflect, and Ponder

7. What happens to the waste products from the Bunsen burner's flame?

8. Which one of the waste products from the Bunsen burner's flame contributes to a global environmental problem? What is the name commonly given to this problem? What kinds of fuels contribute to this problem? Give some examples of these fuels?

Experiment

2

Going Metric With the Rest of the World

Then down with every "metric" scheme   *A perfect inch, a perfect pint,*
Taught by the foreign school,   *The Anglo's honest pound,*
We'll worship still our Father's God!   *Shall hold their place upon the earth,*
And keep our Father's "rule"!   *Till Time's last trump shall sound!*

(From an early anti-metric themesong "A Pint's a Pound the World Around")

Samples From Home

1. Bring a empty can or bottle that has the volume listed on it.

2. Bring ONE of the following: at least 15 mL (1/2 ounce) of a liquid (rubbing alcohol, canned fruit syrup, juice, cleaning solvent, etc.) **or** an equal volume of a solid which will fit into a one inch diameter cylinder (wood, rock, metal, plastic, etc.) **or** equivalent weight of granular solid (do not choose solids which dissolve in water).

3. Bring one small unopened food package on which a net weight is given (bag of peanuts, candy bar, etc.).

Objectives

Various pieces of laboratory apparatus for determining lengths, volumes, and weights will be examined. The "sizes" of familiar units of measurement will be determined in metric units, and English/metric conversion factors calculated from experimental data. The experimental measurement of density will be explored, and the truth-in-packaging of a consumer product determined.

Background

If Miss World of the year 2000 would weigh in at 55 with "measurements" of 91-61-91, does that suggest some radical mutation to have taken place in our evolution during the remainder of this century? It could happen not due to radiation from a nuclear holocaust, but something much less violent although still greatly shaking industrial output, personal habits, and the world economy. All this simply marks the official coming of the metric system to America sometime in the near future.

Did you know that when the U.S. Navy ordered some cannon balls in the last century, in addition to stating the "precise" diameter of the balls in inches, it also included three barleycorns to use as a reference standard for the "precise" inch? Just as the size of barleycorns obviously varies from plant to plant and kernel to kernel, so did the "standard inch". Other equally ludicrous standards exist for other units in the English system which although considerably refined nowadays, still fall far short of the fantastic precision required by science—especially, for example, in the space program.

Wouldn't it be neat to have, say, a unit of length that had an almost infinite degree of exactness, was the same unit used the world over, and which could be converted to smaller or larger units simply by moving the decimal over to the right or left. For instance, think how practical it would be if 1 foot = 10 inches = 0.1 yards. Well that is what the metric system is all about. The system itself has been around for a long time (since 1791), but only now is the United States seriously considering joining the world metric community. Why?

You don't need a chemistry course to tell you that people and their ways and ideas are very resistant to change. Some might call it "tradition". When dealing with a single individual, a degree of physical arm bending could make one break with tradition. With nations of individuals, however, a more political form of arm bending can often be equally effective where all else has failed—that of economics. What could be more English than England, but that country has now essentially completed the enormous job of changing over to the metric system—not just currency; but every nickelodeon, screw, and imperial gallon has received a new metric facelift.

Is there no safe place for tradition and the English system? It is the United States which, in spite of much talk, still remains as the only major nation not officially committed to "going metric". (Besides the United States, only Brunei and Yemen still officially retain the English system).

But we see the economics of world trade finally forcing the last bastions of English measurement system countries to join the rest of the metric world.

Apart from measurement units themselves, density is a concept which is also explored in this experiment. It is not unique to the metric system, but it will be expressed only in metric units in your chemistry course. You would say that lead is heavier than aluminum, right? But you don't really mean just heavier in pounds or grams, because however much weight of lead you wish to imagine, a pile of aluminum of equal weight can be made. What you really mean subconsciously is that given equal volumes of both lead and aluminum, the lead will weigh more. This is what density is all about, and its units do indeed refer to a weight, (to be precise scientists say mass), but it is expressed as a weight per an equal reference volume. Metrically speaking, one cubic centimeter (1 cm³) of lead weighs 11.4 grams, while 1 cm³ of aluminum weighs only 2.7 grams. Scientifically, the density of lead is 11.4 grams per cubic centimeter (11.4 g/cm³), and the density of aluminum is 2.7 g/cm³. Unit–wise, note that to obtain the density of a substance, we must divide weight by volume units (or divide volume units into weight units, if you prefer).

The densities of different substances represent a characteristic physical property identifying that substance, just like a melting point and a boiling point. All samples which are chemically pure water, for example, melt at 0 °C, boil at 100 °C under one atmosphere pressure, and have the same density which is 1.0 g/cm³ = 1.0 g/mL.

Procedure

1. *Length*: Choose any object or accurately measurable distance in the lab between one and three feet long, for example the width of a lab drawer or counter top. Use a combination meter–yard stick and measure the length in both metric and English units to the degree of accuracy specified on the report sheet.

2. *Volume*: Fill your container from home with water to the level of the original liquid and then pour the liquid into a graduated cylinder to determine its total metric volume. Use the larger cylinders available if you have a lot of liquid to measure. Remember when reading volumes in your cylinder to place your eye directly opposite the water level and then take the reading corresponding to the bottom of the concave liquid surface (called the meniscus). Examine the markings on the graduate carefully and decide how many milliliters each single division is worth.

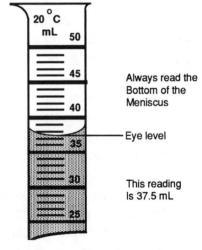

Figure 2.1. *Reading the meniscus.*

Give Them
2.54 cm

And They'll Take
1.61 km

3. *Weight*: You will be given a cylindrical metal bar with a symbol stamped on it representing the chemical element of which the bar is composed. If no symbol is present, your lab instructor will give it to you. Using the triple beam balance as demonstrated by your lab instructor, obtain the weight of your metal bar. Always remember to zero the balance before you start, and to read the balance as accurately as warranted, that is, get all the weight numbers to which you are entitled. This normally will mean an accuracy to at least a hundredth of a gram (0.01 g—to two decimal places).

4. *Density of a metal bar:* In order to calculate the density of your metal bar, you will also need to know its volume. This can be easily measured by determining what volume of water (or any convenient liquid) the bar displaces. Fill your graduated cylinder (25 mL size is best) about half full, and read liquid level to nearest 0.1 mL. Then, inclining the graduate, slide in your bar (please—don't BOMB in your metal—too many graduated cylinder bottoms have been lost that way). The increase in volume will then equal the volume of your metal. You should repeat your measurements if your experimentally determined density does not agree closely (within 10%) with the literature value found in *The Merck Index* or some similar reference, or data in either of the following two tables . (HINT: In many references the abbreviation **d** refers to the density.)

5. *Density of an unknown*: Determine the density of your unknown sample from home by measuring the mass and volume. A simple method for determining liquid densities is to weigh a graduated cylinder empty, then fill it up to a convenient level with your unknown liquid and reweigh. The difference between the two weights equals the net weight of your unknown while its volume is read directly from the graduate. Calculate the density by dividing the mass (weight) by the volume. Liquid densities can also be determined with an hydrometer if it is available. See your lab instructor for this.

If you know or can estimate the possible identity of your sample from home, look up its accepted density with help from the tables on the following two pages.

6. Truth-in-packaging: Complete the data called for on the report sheet for your "goodies." (Yes, you may eat this one experiment!)

Density of Various Liquids*

Liquid	Grams per cm^3	Pounds per $ft.^3$	Temp °C
Acetone	0.792	49.4	20
Alcohol, ethyl	0.791	49.4	20
Alcohol, methyl	0.810	50.5	0
Benzene	0.899	56.1	0
Carbolic acid	0.950-0.965	59.2-60.2	15
Carbon disulfide	1.293	80.7	0
Carbon tetrachloride	1.595	99.6	20
Chloroform	1.489	93.0	20
Ether	0.736	45.9	0
Gasoline	0.66-0.69	41.0-43.0	
Glycerine	1.260	78.6	0
Kerosene	0.82	51.2	
Mercury	13.6	849.0	
Milk	1.028-1.035	64.2-64.6	
Naphtha, petroleum ether	0.665	41.5	15
Naphtha, wood	0.848-0.810	52.9-50.5	0
Oil, castor	0.969	60.5	15
Oil, cocoanut	0.925	57.7	15
Oil, cotton seed	0.926	57.8	16
Oil, creosote	1.040-1.100	64.9-68.9	15
Oil, linseed, boiled	0.942	58.8	15
Oil, olive	0.918	57.3	15
Sea water	1.025	63.99	15
Turpentine (spirits)	0.87	54.3	
Water	1.00	62.43	4

*Reprinted with permission from *CRC Handbook of Chemistry & Physics, 51st Edition*, 1970–71. Copyright © CRC Press, Inc., Boca Raton, FL.

Density of Various Solids*

Substance	Grams per cu. cm	Pounds per cu. ft.	Substance	Grams per cu. cm	Pounds per cu. ft.
Agate	2.5-2.7	156-168	Diamond	3.01-3 52	188-220
Alabaster, carbonate	2.69-2.78	168-173	Dolomite	2.84	177
Alabaster, sulfate	2.26-2.32	141-145	Ebonite	1.15	72
Albite	2.62-2.65	163-165	Emery	4.0	250
Amber	1.06-1.11	66-69	Epidote	3.25-3.50	203-218
Amphiboles	2.9-3.2	180-200	Feldspar	2.55-2.75	159-172
Anorthite	2.74-2.76	171-172	Flint	2.63	164
Asbestos	2.0-2.8	125-175	Fluorite	3.18	198
Asbestos slate	1.8	112	Galena	7.3-7.6	460-470
Asphalt	1.1-1.5	69-94	Gamboge	1.2	75
Basalt	2.4-3.1	150-190	Garnet	3.15-4.3	197-268
Beeswax	0.96-0.97	60-61	Gas carbon	1.88	117
Beryl	2.69-2.7	168-169	Gelatin	1.27	79
Biotite	2.7-3.1	170-190	Glass, common	2.4-2.8	150-175
Bone	1.7-2.0	106-125	Glass, flint	2.9-5.9	180-370
Brick	1 4-2.2	87-137	Glue	1.27	79
Butter	0.86-0.87	53-54	Granite	2.64-2.76	165-172
Calamine	4.1-4.5	255-280	Gum arabic	1.3-1.4	81-87
Calcspar	2.6-2.8	162-175	Gypsum	2.31-2.72	144-145
Camphor	0.99	62	Hematite	4.9-5.3	306-330
Caoutchouc	0.92-0.99	57-62	Hornblend	3.0	187
Cardboard	O.69	43	Ice	0.917	57.2
Celluloid	1. 4	87	Ivory	1.83-1.92	114-120
Cement, set	2.7-3.0	170-190	Leather, dry	0.86	54
Chalk	1.9-2.8	118-175	Lime, slaked	1.3-1.4	81-87
Charcoal, oak	0.57	35	Limestone	2.68-2.76	167-171
Charcoal, pine	0.28—0.44	18—28	Linoleum	1.18	74
Cinnabar	8.12	507	Magnetite	4.9-5.2	306-324
Clay	1.8-2.6	112-162	Malachite	3.74.1	231-256
Coal, anthracite	1. 4-1. 8	87-112	Marble	2.6-2.84	160-177
Coal, bituminous	1.2-1.5	75-94	Meerschaum	0.99-1.28	62-80
Cocoa butter	0.89-0.91	56-57	Mica	2.6-3.2	165-200
Coke	1.0-1.7	62-105	Muscovite	2.76-3.00	172-187
Copal	1.04-1.14	65-71	Ochre	3.5	218
Cork	0.22-0.26	14-16	Opal	2.2	137
Cork linoleum	0.54	34	Paper	0.7-1.15	44-72
Corundum	3.9-4.0	245-250	Paraffin	0.87-0.91	54-57

*Reprinted with permission from *CRC Handbook of Chemistry & Physics*, *51st Edition*, 1970–71. Copyright © CRC Press, Inc., Boca Raton, FL.

Density of Various Solids (*continued*)

Substance	Grams per cu. cm	Pounds per cu. ft.	Substance	Grams per cu. cm	Pounds per cu. ft.
Peat blocks	0.84	52	Wood (continued)		
Pitch	1.07	67	birch	0.51-0.77	32-48
Porcelain	2.3-2.5	143-156	blue gum	1.00	62
Porphyry	2.6-2.9	162-181	box	0.95-1.16	59-72
Pressed wood pulp board	0.19	12	butternut	0.38	24
Pyrite	4.95-5.1	309-318	cedar	0.49-0.57	30-35
Quartz	2.65	165	cherry	0.70-0.90	43-56
Resin	I.07	67	dogwood	0 76	47
Rock salt	2.18	136	ebony	1.11-1.33	69-83
Rubber, hard	1.19	74	elm	0.54-0.60	34-37
Rubber, soft, commercial	1.1	69	hickory	0.60-0.93	37-58
Sandstone	2.14-2.36	134-147	juniper	0.56	35
Serpentine	2.50-2.65	156-165	larch	0.50-0.56	31-35
Silica, fused transparent	2.21	138	lignum vitae	1.17-1.33	73-83
Silica, fused translucent	2.07	129	locust	0.67-0.71	42-44
Slag	2.0-3.9	125-240	logwood	0.91	57
Slate	2.6-3.3	162-205	mahogany, Honduras	0.66	41
Soapstone	2.6-2.8	162-175	mahogany, Spanish	0.85	53
Spermaceti	0.95	59	maple	0.62-0.75	39-47
Starch	1.53	95	oak	0.60-0.90	37-56
Sugar	1.59	99	pear	0.61-O.73	38-45
Talc	2.7-2.8	168-174	pine, pitch	0.83-0.85	52-53
Tallow, beef	0.94	59	pine, white	0.35-0.50	22-31
Tallow, mutton	0.94	59	pine, yellow	0.37-0.60	23-37
Tar	1.02	66	plum	0.66 0.78	41-49
Topaz	3.5-3.6	219-223	poplar	0.35-0.5	22-31
Tourmaline	3.0-3.2	190-200	satinwood	0.95	59
Wax, sealing	1.8	112	spruce	0.48-0.70	30-44
Wood (seasoned)			sycamore	0.40-0.60	24-37
alder	0.42-0.68	26-42	teak, Indian	0.66-0.88	41-55
apple	0.66-0.84	41-52	teak. African	0.98	61
ash	0.65-0.85	40-53	walnut	0.64-0.70	40-43
balsa	0.11-0.14	7-9	water gum	1.00	62
bamboo	0.31-0.40	19-25	willow	0.40-0.60	24-37
basswood	O.32-0 59	20-37			
beech	O.70-0.90	43-56			

Report Sheet—Experiment 2
Going Metric

Date _____   **Section number** _____   **Name** _____

1. Length of object or distance

   (a) To nearest 0.1 centimeter _____cm.

   (b) To nearest 0.1 inches _____in.

   (c) Calculated number of centimeters in 1 inch
   (just the cm per inch conversion factor; divide line 1(a) by line 1(b)) =
   _____cm/in.

2. Volume of container

   (a) To nearest 1 milliliter _____mL.

   (b) Calculated actual volume of container in ounces obtained from following:
   (multiply mL in Line 2(a) by 0.0338 oz/mL) =
   _____oz.

   (c) Volume stamped on the container itself _____.

   (d) Based on your data in (b) and (c) above, does this container give you your "volumes worth"? _____

3. Weight of known metal bar to nearest 0.01g _____g.

4. Density of a known

   Final volume of water with bar in cylinder (estimated to 0.1mL) _____mL.

   Initial volume of water in cylinder without bar (to nearest 0.1mL) _____mL.

   (a) Volume of metal bar (Final water volume - Initial volume) _____mL.

   (b) Calculated density of bar (line 3 divided by line 4(a)) = _____g/mL or g/cm^3.
   (These units are equivalent since 1mL = 1 cm^3).

   (c) Identity of metal (from symbol on bar) _____.

   (d) Accepted density of this metal (from reference) _____g/cm^3.

5. Density of an unknown

   Nature of sample _____.

   Weight of sample   _____g.

   Volume of sample   _____mL = cm³.

   (a) Calculated density of unknown (mass divided by volume)   _____g/cm³.

   (b) Does this value for density seem reasonable?

Look up densities of similar substances on pages 20, 21, and 22 in the density tables. Also, all water based (aqueous) solutions will have a density very close to that for pure water—1.00 grams per milliliter.)

6. Truth—in—packaging:

   Brand and nature of food product _____.

   Weight of package and contents (to nearest 0.0lg)   _____g.

   Weight of package less contents   _____g.

   (a) Net weight of contents (from your data above)   _____g.

   (b) Stated net weight (from label)   _____g.

   (c) If weight in 6(b), is in ounces, you will have to convert to grams:
   (line 6(b) ounces multiplied by 28.3 grams/ounce) =   _____g.

   (d) Does this package truthfully offer you your "grams worth" of goodies?

7. Conclusions and comments regarding this experiment

30 g of Prevention Is Worth 0.454 kg of Cure

Questions—Experiment 2
Going Metric

Date _____   Section number _____   Name _____

1. Using the same basic procedure of liquid displacement, describe how the volume of 10 grams of sugar might be determined experimentally in the lab. Hint: Water displacement method could not be used since when solids dissolve in a liquid, the volumes are not additive.

2. Polychlorinated biphenyls (PCB's) are a type of chlorinated hydrocarbons having densities around 1.3-1.4 g/cm^3. They are not an insecticide (like DDT) but are used as a transformer coolant oil; however, their potential danger to the environment appears to exceed that of DDT. Not only are they very resistant to biodegradation, if spilled into water PCB's pose a much more difficult clean up problem than, say, oil. Explain why given the fact that the density of water is 1.0 g/cm^3.

3. In what units of measurement would Miss World's statistics most likely be reported? (See the background.)

4. Write the English equivalent of these metricized expressions:

   (a) 30 g of prevention is worth 0.454 kg of cure;

   (b) Give them 2.54 cm and they'll take 1.61 km.

Think, Speculate, Reflect, and Ponder

5. Just what **is** the advantage of having everyone on the planet using the same units of measurements?

6. Why do you think that the United States has been so slow in adopting the metric system?

Experiment

3

Recycling Aluminum Chemically

Samples From Home

1. Bring aluminum from a used consumer product (beverage can, TV dinner plate, or pie tin).

2. Bring an object with a painted or varnished surface for testing the effectiveness of your synthesized paint remover (a yellow pencil is fine).

Objectives

The recyclability of "used" aluminum atoms will be illustrated by chemically converting waste aluminum packaging into a new compound and isolating the final product using the technique of suction filtration. This compound will be added to an organic solvent and the effectiveness of the resulting solution as a paint/varnish remover will be tested.

Background

Much is heard of recycling nowadays. Since our natural resources on **spaceship Earth** are decidedly finite, we cannot indefinitely continue as a throw-away society. We must develop a recycle mentality, and it should be encouraged and rewarded by economic incentives and public respect and appreciation. Unfortunately, any rapid movement towards large public acceptance and demand for changes in basic life-styles requires revolution or crisis, and it is difficult to impress people with a crisis <u>before</u> it happens.

All this might be largely overcome, however, if the costs of recycling goods were significantly cheaper than obtaining them from virgin (or at least natural) resources. Recycling for most things cannot be made sufficiently attractive economically to compete successfully on the mass scale necessary especially because of pressures to continue special tax breaks for companies extracting natural resources from the earth, and because of reduced rate transportation costs for "natural" resources (as opposed to "unnatural", or used resources—i.e., recyclables). Garbage, paper, plastic, cardboard, tin cans, glass, magazines—most or all of these *can* be recycled by the consumers if they are willing to persevere and find their way to the "nearest" centers accepting these goods.

But as such recycle-minded consumers are aware, oft times different centers must be sought out for different goods, the nearest may lie very far away indeed, and they must be willing to receive little or nothing in the way of money for their labors. Therefore, at this point in time, the recycling of most things for most people must be more an act of conscience and concern for their future and their environment, rather than thought of any monetary gain. This is especially true since increased recycling activity has reduced prices paid to consumers—the law of supply and demand!

Trash disposal companies are now beginning to provide curbside recycling in some parts of the country for paper, cardboard, aluminum, steel ("tin") cans, yard debris, and plastic bottles with the numbers 1 or 2 on the bottom. Some states have passed beverage container deposit laws; recycle programs are being established in the work place; and cities are making efforts towards recycling which could help their "Where to we put our garbage" crisis. So the momentum is building—with a little help from crisis economics and the desire for a less polluted environment.

One cast-away that appears to be a possible exception, however, is aluminum. Because of its relatively high initial cost, the great amount of energy required in order to obtain it in a pure state from its natural ores, and its very light weight, this metal is able to compete economically with "natural" aluminum from ores, and the consumer has been paid 20 to 50 cents a pound for it. The recycling of aluminum consumes only 5% as much energy as that needed to liberate aluminum metal from its natural ores.

"A rose is a rose is a rose" is a saying familiar to many. Likewise, "An aluminum atom is an aluminum atom is an aluminum atom." Used, unused, heated, burned, stomped, or pounded—all aluminum atoms must remain aluminum. Thus the second-hand "used" atom lot can be a place for real bargain hunters since the second-hand product is identical to the original. Where else besides a "used atom mart" can one find such a deal?

You begin by "dissolving" (actually, chemically reacting) your sample of aluminum with hydrochloric acid:

$$2Al \quad + \quad 6HCl \quad \longrightarrow \quad 2AlCl_3 \quad + \quad 3H_2$$

aluminum   hydrochloric acid   aluminum chloride   hydrogen gas
(insoluble)   (water solution)   (soluble)   (bubbles)

The amount of aluminum metal specified in the directions is twice as much as can react completely with the acid, so do not expect all the metal to disappear. The aluminum in aluminum chloride will then be in the form of positive aluminum ions, and when mixed with appropriate negative ions, can combine with them to yield an insoluble precipitate. The particular negative ions chosen are those which will form special kinds of aluminum salts having the ability to thicken many organic liquids so much that they will even form a gel. These substances, effective at low concentrations, are aluminum salts of certain organic acids, and they find a multitude of uses spanning the full moral spectrum of good to evil, from the manufacture of jellied solutions for removing dead paint to the production of jellied napalm for removing live flesh from human beings.

The particular organic acids used to make these aluminum compounds in this experiment will be those found in Ivory soap. Actually, the sodium salts of these organic acids are what comprise the soap, whose principle ingredient is the sodium salt of stearic acid—sodium stearate. But Ivory soap is not pure sodium stearate. The label may say 99 and 44/100% pure, but pure what one should ask! In addition to this, the reaction itself can proceed in several steps giving several different, albeit similar, products. Thus the product you isolate is not a pure compound, but a mixture of several compounds.

Chemically, the reaction itself is not unlike that which occurs between soap and certain other ions (calcium and magnesium) which are found in hard water. Compounds containing these ions give us the "bathtub ring." Both of the following reactions probably occur to some extent in your preparation:

$$H_2O \; + \; AlCl_3 \; + \; 2Na\,C_{18}H_{35}O_2 \; \longrightarrow \; Al(C_{18}H_{35}O_2)_2OH \; + \; 2NaCl \; + \; HCl$$

$$2H_2O \; + \; AlCl_3 \; + \; Na\,C_{18}H_{35}O_2 \; \longrightarrow \; Al(C_{18}H_{35}O_2)(OH)_2 + \; NaCl \; + \; 2HCl$$

water   aluminum   sodium stearate   aluminum stearate   sodium   (gas)
       chloride   (soluble)   complex salts   chloride
       (soluble)   (insoluble)   (soluble)

Warming the solution containing the precipitate enhances its thickening power and helps coagulate it into small particles which can be lifted from the surface. The acetone wash removes adhering water and permits rapid drying of the precipitate so that it can be quickly tested as an organic solvent thickening agent. (You might like to try pouring a little acetone—nail polish remover ingredient—on your hand to observe how quickly it evaporates and cools your skin). A mixture of organic solvents is then added to your aluminum salt to form the thick liquid or gel necessary for a good paint remover. It is actually these solvents themselves (mainly methylene chloride) that work their way underneath the paint film and "lift" it off. But if these solvents were not made into a jelly consistency, they would quickly run off of the surface and evaporate before they had time to do their paint removing job.

Many commercial paint removers have, in addition to methylene chloride as the main ingredient, other compounds to enhance their solvent power and thickening ability, such as aromatics, alcohols, etc. The particular formulation used in this experiment is typical and can be found in *Bennett's The Chemical Formulary*—a multivolume encyclopedic reference which offers how-to-make and ingredient information on a multitude of products from adhesives to window cleaners. (You might like to browse through, some of the *Formulary* volumes next time you are in a library.)

Aluminum ions can also be used to make gels to thicken water. When mixed with hydroxide ions (OH⁻) found in alkaline (basic) solutions, the following reaction occurs:

$$Al^{+3} \quad + \quad 3OH^- \quad \longrightarrow \quad Al(OH)_3$$

aluminum ions   hydroxide ions   aluminum hydroxide (jelly)

But the jelly is very touchy—too much (or too little) hydroxide will make the gel disappear. Particles of this cheap aluminum gel have been used to clarify lakes and reservoirs by sticking suspended sediments to the gel's surface as it falls to the bottom.

Procedure

1. Weigh out about 1 gram of aluminum from your food/beverage container into a 100 mL beaker (exactness not necessary since an excess of metal is used). Use the sides of aluminum beverage cans.

Aluminum parts often have an obvious coating of paint or lacquer on them which will retard its reaction with acid. Scrape off 3/4 of the coating with a knife or razor blade. Cut up into small pieces if

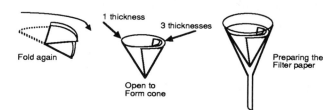

Figure 3.1. *Folding filter paper.*

necessary, or press down so that your sample lies flat on the bottom of the beaker and can be completely covered by the acid.

    (a) Place your beaker plus sample in a hood and, using a 10 mL graduate, add 10 mL of dilute (6*M*) HCl. A vigorous reaction will occur immediately or within 20-30 seconds depending upon your particular aluminum sample. Swirl the beaker contents periodically until the reaction has ceased or becomes very sluggish (about 10 minutes). Record your observations of this reaction.

2. Add 20 mL of water to your reaction solution, mix well with a stirring rod, and gravity filter (use a 12.5 cm filter paper cone fitted inside of your funnel). Catch the liquid in a 125 mL Erlenmeyer flask. This clear liquid (called "filtrate") represents your recycled aluminum stock solution.

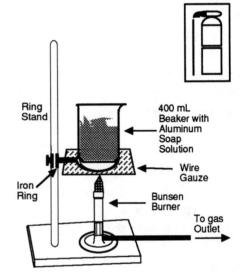

(a) Pour 200 mL of a 0.5% soap solution into a 400 mL beaker. While stirring vigorously with a spatula or glass rod, add to this beaker 5 mL of your aluminum stock solution. Note your observations. Save the aluminum stock solution left over to recoup any "goofs" and to complete **Part 4** at the end of the experiment.

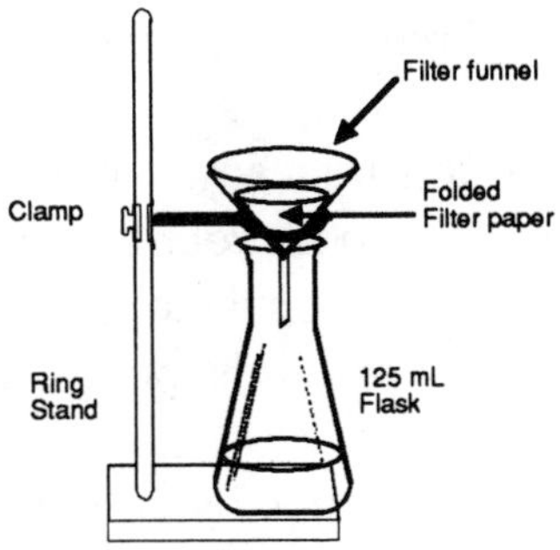

Figure 3.2 *Gravity filtration set-up.*

Place the beaker of solution containing precipitate onto a wire gauze mounted on a ring and heat as rapidly as possible with a Bunsen burner placed directly underneath. Stir every couple of minutes.

Slightly before or as soon as the liquid begins to boil, (WATCH CAREFULLY SO THE SOLUTION DOES NOT BOIL OVER) turn off the heat and with a scoopula skim off the granular precipitate which has risen to the surface. Transfer this solid directly into a 400 mL beaker about 1/2 full of cold water and break up any lumps with the scoopula.

You will now filter the solid from the cold water solution using the technique of suction filtration. Your instructor will demonstrate this procedure, but the essential steps follow.

Figure 3.3. *Heating aluminum solution filtrate with soap.*

Obtain a 250 mL or 500 mL suction flask, 7 cm diameter Büchner funnel, rubber "O" ring and filter paper (5.5 cm paper circles), to fit inside the funnel.

Clamp your flask to a ring stand to prevent overturning. Hook up the suction flask to the water aspirator with the heavy wall rubber tubing provided. Place the "O" ring onto top of the flask with the tapered hole pointing down.

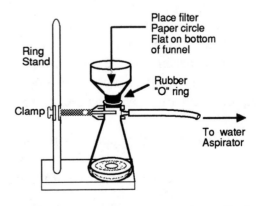

Figure 3.4. *Büchner funnel and filter flask for suction filtration.*

Insert the Büchner funnel and drop the filter paper in place so all the holes are covered. Wet the filter paper with water (sprinkling with your hand is OK); turn on the water FULL, and press down on the funnel until you can feel the suction take hold. Place palm of hand flat across funnel mouth to test this.

Now you are ready to proceed with the filtration of your sample. With the suction applied as described, pour your beaker contents into the funnel as rapidly as the liquid is sucked through. Use your scoopula to transfer any remaining bits of solid. (Your instructor can assist you if the filtration proceeds too slowly due to a plugged filter paper.)

Stop the suction by turning off the water. Add approximately 10 mL of acetone directly to the white solid in your funnel (CAUTION: *Flammable liquid. Make sure that there are no flames within 4 feet of your apparatus.*) Gently (so as not to tear the filter paper) mix the precipitate with acetone using the blunt end of a solid glass rod. Turn on the water again and hold down sides of funnel until the suction takes hold and pulls all the acetone through the paper. Maintain the suction for two minutes. Discard filtrate and save the white solid in Büchner funnel.

Weigh a 50 mL beaker to the nearest 0.01 gram. Dump/scrape your solid aluminum soap pre-cipitate (left in funnel) into this beaker and place the beaker into a drying oven for 5 minutes at 150 °C. Remove the beaker from the oven using tongs or paper toweling to prevent burning your hands on the hot beaker and let it cool to room temperature. The solid should be bone dry and have no acetone smell whatsoever.

(b) Note the texture and appearance of this solid (color, crystal form if any, etc.).

(c) and **(d)** Reweigh the beaker plus contents to the nearest 0.01 gram and report the net increase in weight as the weight of precipitate on report sheet. Also calculate the percent yield using the formula given on the report sheet.

3. Thoroughly powder your white solid aluminum soap precipitate by mashing with a scoopula. Then pour 5 mL of the "solvent mixture" solution into a DRY 10 mL graduate. (If necessary; dry by rinsing with a little acetone and allow to drain).

With the aid of a capillary dropping pipette (long nose medicine dropper), add the solvent mix-ture solution to the white powder in your 50 mL beaker in roughly 1/2 to 1 milliliter portions, stirring & mashing up the powder/liquid mixture after each portion is added. STOP adding more solvent when the beaker contents attain a honey/jelly consistency. (Expect each 0.1 g of solid to require about 1 mL of solvent; e.g., 0.5 g solid needs 5 mL solvent)

(a) Record the approximate volume of solvent added.

(b) Note the appearance of the gel.

(c) Spread your solvent mixture/aluminum soap complex salt "solution" from **3(a)** onto a painted or varnished surface and allow to it stand 5-10 minutes while doing **Part 4.** (A common yellow painted pencil works fine) Evaluate its effectiveness as a paint remover.

4. Add dilute ammonium hydroxide (6M NH$_4$OH) to the unused remainder of the aluminum stock solution in the 125 mL Erlenmeyer flask. Squirt the ammonium hydroxide into the flask with a medicine dropper while continuously swirling. When the proper amount (not more, not less) of NH$_4$OH has been added, aluminum hydroxide will have formed and the "liquid" at this point should be so thick that it will not pour. Record your observations on the nature of Al(OH)$_3$ on the report sheet.

Report Sheet—Experiment 3
Recycling Aluminum Chemically

Date _____   **Section number** _____   **Name** _____

Source of your aluminum sample_____

1. What is the evidence indicating a chemical reaction between solid aluminum and the added hydrochloric acid?

2. Aluminum solution + soap

    (a) Observations upon addition

    (b) Texture and appearance of dried precipitate

    (c) Weight of dry precipitate   _____g.

    (d) Per cent yield (grams in line 2(c) is what %
    of the maximum possible yield, about 1.0 g.)
    (Line 2(c) divided by 1.0 g then multiply by 100)   _____%.

3. Formation of a gel

    (a) Volume of solvent mixture added to powder   _____mL.

    (b) Appearance/nature of the gel

    (c) Comments on the effectiveness of above "solution" as paint remover.

4. What is the observed nature of $Al(OH)_3$?

5. Comments and conclusions on experiment

Questions—Experiment 3
Recycling Aluminum Chemically

Date _____ Section number _____ Name _____

1. Does the aluminum really "dissolve" in the hydrochloric acid? Explain for credit.

2. Why does an organic thickening agent enhance the effectiveness of organic solvents as paint removers?

3. Check the *Merck Index* for other uses (2) for aluminum stearate.

(a)

(b)

Think, Speculate, Reflect, and Ponder

4. Why doesn't the Unites States just pass a law requiring that no more virgin aluminum be used in products sold in the United States?

5. Considering the law of supply and demand, what will have to happen to make the price paid for recycled products rise? Can you play a part in this in any way?

6. What uses for aluminum are depicted in the sketch* that appears below?

*Sketch reprinted with permission from *Contemporary Chemistry*, E. A. Walters and E. M. Wewerka, Merrill-MacMillan Publishers. Copyright Edward A. Walters.

Experiment

4

Radioactivity

Sample From Home

No samples from home are required for this experiment.

Objectives

This thought experiment will give you an idea of your annual dosage of radiation and may give you a few things to think about during the ensuing debate by the lab class on nuclear power generation of electricity.

Background

Radioactive decay is as natural as the universe itself. As a matter of fact, the majority of the known nuclides (or isotopes—particular arrangements of protons and neutrons in a nucleus) <u>are</u> radioactive. There are about 2000 known nuclides and less than 15% of these are stable and not radioactive. The effects of radioactivity on human beings, however, can be quite dangerous.

Radiation that is sufficiently energetic can damage human tissue by ionization, dissociation, and excitation of the molecules in the tissue. This can cause the death or extensive damage of this tissue. In addition to the outright killing of tissue cells, the damage that radiation does can take place in the genes—that part of the cell that carries the instructions for reproduction. This may lead to cancer.

The natural background radiation that we are exposed to from birth (actually from conception) comes from sources like the building materials that surround us everyday, cosmic radiation entering the earth's atmosphere from space, and the food we eat containing radioactive elements from natural sources. These factors are all very low and vary somewhat based on your location on the planet. People who live in stone buildings are, for instance, exposed to more radiation than those who live in wooden structures. Likewise, people who live at high altitudes are exposed to higher levels of cosmic radiation than those who live at sea level because there is less of the protective blanket of the atmosphere between them and space.

Background radiation from natural sources has not changed and probably will not change significantly over time. It is determined by the composition of the earth (and in the case of cosmic radiation, our planets position in the solar system and the universe). The amount of radiation from "man-made" sources, however, has been on the increase ever since the explosion of the first atomic bombs in 1945. (The materials that are referred to here were of course not really made by human beings but were merely mined and refined from natural deposits or made by the reactions of naturally radioactive elements.) Until the Atmospheric Test Ban Treaty was put into effect in 1963, nuclear weapons test were often carried out at the surface of the earth where the radioactive products of these massive explosions could contaminate the air, soil, and water. Between 1946 and 1963 the United States conducted 66 open air nuclear tests in the Marshall Islands in the Pacific Ocean and 183 in Nevada in the United States. Since the Atmospheric Test Ban Treaty, nuclear weapons testing has been limited to underground explosions which are generally not vented to the atmosphere, although this has happened by accident on a number of occasions.

In addition to radiation releases from nuclear weapons testing, the advent of electricity generation from nuclear power has increased the background radiation by an undetermined amount. In the case of the increased radiation dosage per human being, the increased amount averaged over the entire population of a country or hemisphere or especially the entire world is vanishingly small when compared to the natural background radiation that is already present. However, for individuals who live near the site of a nuclear accident (for example Chernobyl in the USSR) the increase in radiation dosage may be quite significantly increased.

Finally, don't forget to consider the contribution to our radiation exposure from extremely useful medical tools such as X-rays. These also increase our radiation exposure to some degree based on the amount of X-ray procedures performed, the equipment used, and the part of the body imaged by this technique. Though this exposure to radiation is not really a natural consequence of living in our environment, it is after all a choice that we make to have these techniques used. Few people choose not to be exposed to this sort of radiation because they believe the test to be necessary.

The biological effects of radiation can be measured in many different ways. One of the units of measurement is called the roentgen equivalent man (rem). On thousandth of a rem is a millirem (mrem). The table below shows a few estimates of the annual exposures of human beings to different sources of radiation measured in millirems. Note that these are just a few of a number of widely varying estimates and are not meant to reflect accurate, well-known values. They are only provided to give you an idea of the sources of radiation exposure in your life and the possible relative contribution from each. Also note that these values are an average and may very well not reflect dosages of individuals acutely exposed because of weapons test venting, close proximity to coal fired power plants, repeated medical X-rays, etc.

Various Estimated Radiation Exposures

Sources of Radiation	Average annual dose in millirems
Terrestrial	63
Cosmic Rays	43
Medical X-rays	90
Burning of Fossil Fuels	2
Fallout from weapons testing	4

Report Sheet—Experiment 4
Radioactivity

Date _____   **Section number** _____   **Name** _____

Class discussion of nuclear power generation in the United States

A recent letter to the editor in a widely read magazine stated flatly that the letter's author was tired of hearing and reading that individuals calling themselves "environmentalists" were opposed to the use of nuclear power to generate electricity in the United States. The writer said that anyone who opposed nuclear power (in the Northeast) was in effect choosing brownouts and power failures and this, he stated, was an obviously anti-environmental position since many people's lives depend on a relatively constant flow of electricity (hospitals, drug storage, food preservation, etc.). The author concluded that of all the present energy methods to supply mass power grids, nuclear power was the cleanest and safest means presently available in the United States.

To begin with, do you agree or disagree with this author's position? Why or why not? Discussion should initially be focused upon this point but can go farther afield. Areas such as alternate means of power generation, pollution factors, waste storage, and health concerns are all fair game for this discussion. All members of the laboratory will be expected to express an opinion on the initial question at least, but involvement and participation in this discussion will not be forced beyond the answering of the initial question. Prior reading and preparation are encouraged for this laboratory "experiment".

Questions—Experiment 4
Radioactivity

Date _____   Section number _____   Name _____

Think, Speculate, Reflect, and Ponder

1. The public debate about the generation of electricity from nuclear power has been raging for over a decade. Why is this such a charged question?

2. One of the solutions to the disposal of nuclear waste would be to fire these materials into space using automated rockets that fly either into deep space or into our sun. Why has this alternative been so strongly discounted *in the last few years*?

3. In the early 1990's there has been an upsurge in the support for nuclear power (at least from the major utility consortia and engineering and design companies). What happened *in the summers* of the last four or five years of the 1980's that helped this resurgence?

Experiment

5

O₂ Content of Air

Sample From Home

No samples from home are needed for this experiment.

Objectives

The percentage of oxygen in normal atmospheric air will be determined using a simple method. This technique makes use of the catalyzed oxidation (rusting) of iron in a closed atmosphere.

Background

The oxygen content (molecular oxygen, O_2) of our atmosphere is something that we seldom think about, yet something that is very important. A large number of the organisms on the planet depend on the oxygen in the air for life. Some organisms remove oxygen from water solutions simply by the diffusion of dissolved oxygen through the membranes of the organism's cells (for example, protozoa and some kinds of worms). Larger life forms need a more specialized way to transfer oxygen into their bodies and to get waste products like carbon dioxide out of their bodies. Many marine animals have gills for this purpose to extract dissolved oxygen from the water that they live in. Some gills (like those that starfish have) are passive absorbers of oxygen and rely on water that is passing by to come in contact with the gill surface to supply the needed oxygen. Other kinds of fish (like sunfish and catfish) optimize this situation by pumping water through their gills. This process is assisted by the fish's movement through the water.

The largest animals on the planet need an even more efficient means of extracting the oxygen that they need from the air (instead of O_2 dissolved in water). Lungs have developed for this purpose. They get the oxygen they need directly, by breathing air into their lungs and selectively removing the oxygen from the other gases (mainly nitrogen and a small amount of carbon dioxide). Human beings, obviously, fall into this last class, and we too are extremely dependent on the oxygen content of the air we breathe.

People who go snow skiing only once a year often have a headache during their first day on the slopes. The reason for this is that most ski slopes are in the mountains at relatively high elevations. As you move higher and higher into the atmosphere the air gets less and less dense: The heaviest air is near the bottom on the atmosphere at the surface of the earth, and the lightest air is at the top of the atmosphere. Some of the "missing" density at higher altitudes is due to a lower oxygen content in the air. Performing a relatively high impact activity like snow skiing demands a lot of oxygen. Although skiers may not notice the lower oxygen content, their bodies often do and respond with a headache. People who have spent an extended time in this lower oxygen atmosphere have developed additional lung capacity to increase their ability to extract the oxygen that they need from the thinner air.

The rusting (oxidation) of iron usually takes place slowly. This process is accelerated by moisture and acidity. The procedure in this experiment takes advantage of both of these catalysts. (Catalysts are reagents that speed up a reaction but are not used up by the reaction itself.) The controlled oxidation of iron is performed in a moist, slightly acidic atmosphere, and the amount of oxygen necessary for the reaction is measured by the "reverse displacement" of water. As oxygen is taken out of the air by the rusting iron, the vacuum produced sucks water up into the inverted graduated to take its place. The percentage of oxygen in the air can then be calculated from the "sucked up water volume" compared to the original air volume of the graduated cylinder.

Procedure

1. Determine the weight of a piece of weighing paper. Record the weight to 0.01g.

2. Wash your hands with soap and water and dry them. Get a piece of steel wool about 1/4 as large as your fist from the supply cart or stockroom. Pinch off a single piece between two fingers and roll it into a little ball in the palm of your hand. Place approximately 0.75 g of steel wool rolled into a ball on the weighing paper and record the total weight to 0.01g. (This piece should be about as large as the end of your thumb, but the size of the ball actually depends on how tightly you roll the ball.) This weight shouldn't be any larger than 1.0 g and no less than

0.5 g. If you end up with a larger or smaller steel wool ball, pinch off a piece or add a small piece to your ball to get approximately 0.75 g. Don't weigh the small pieces that break off. Throw these away and return the larger pieces that you don't use to the supply cart or stockroom.

3. Measure 35 mL of 0.2 *M* acetic acid (vinegar solution) with a graduate cylinder and pour this entire volume into a 50 mL beaker. Keep the beaker in the vent hood. Using your tweezers, put the steel wool ball weighed out in **Step 2** into the acetic acid making sure it is completely covered by the acid. You may have to press down on the ball to completely submerge it.

4. Leave the steel wool in the acid for 1 minute. Remove the acid dipped steel wool from the acetic acid solution with your tweezers; put it in a clean 50 mL beaker and take it back to your work station or bench top. Do not wash off the steel wool after the acid dip.

5. As quickly as possible, remove the acid dipped steel wool ball from your 50 mL beaker using your tweezers and <u>loosely</u> pack the steel wool down into the *bottom* of a 25 mL graduated cylinder. Invert the graduate and set it down into an *empty* 250 mL beaker. Using your wash bottle, add water to the beaker until the lip of the graduated cylinder (including the pour spout) is just covered by water. Be careful not to knock over the inverted graduate.

For this next step use a ruler marked in mm. Set the ruler on the bench top next to the beaker containing the inverted graduate and measure the distance from the bench top to the top of the water that you have added to the beaker. You will need to place a ruler on the bench top outside of the beaker and sight from the water level in the beaker over to the ruler's marks. Use the millimeters side of the ruler instead of the inches side. This will be a small number, probably less than 10 mm. This is your initial water height. Record this value on the report sheet in the appropriate place.

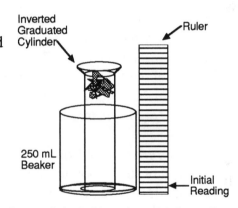

Figure 5.1. *Taking the initial reading.*

As the oxidation (rusting that you have initiated by moistening the steel wool with water and acid) begins, the reaction will use up oxygen in the air inside the graduated cylinder. You will be able to see this because the water level *inside* the graduate will creep up: Oxygen will be used in the reaction and the volume of gases inside the graduate will decrease, pulling water up into the graduate from the beaker.

6. Start watching the clock as soon as you have inverted the graduate and finished measuring the initial water level. About every minute, carefully add water to the beaker with your wash bottle to make the water level *inside the graduated cylinder* and the water level in the beaker exactly level with each other. (If the water level starts to move so radically that there is a chance that the water level *in the beaker* will drop below the spout of the inverted graduate and will allow air to get sucked into the graduate instead of water, add water to the beaker with your wash bottle before the next minute mark.) After five minutes, stop making water additions with your wash bottle every minute and instead add water to even out the water levels every five minutes.

Again, be careful not to tip over the inverted graduate. Continue adding water every five minutes until the reaction stops (about 20 minutes total), and the level of water inside the graduate does not rise any more.

7. When the reaction is completed (no more change in water level since your last leveling addition of water), measure the height of the present water level in the graduate *above the bench top*. In other words, get the height of the water level above where the ruler starts. Place the ruler on the bench top outside of the beaker and sight from the final water level in the beaker (which will exactly match the height inside the graduate if you made your last addition carefully) over to the ruler's marks. Record this reading in millimeters on the report sheet in the appropriate place. The difference between the initial and final readings will therefore be the distance that the water has travelled up into the graduated cylinder during the whole reaction time.

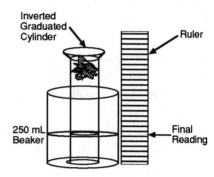

Figure 5.2. *Taking the final reading.*

After you have successfully measured the distance that the water level has traveled, remove the steel wool from the graduated cylinder and discard it in the appropriate waste container. With your ruler measure the total height of the cylinder *from the lip to the top of the base*. Record this value in millimeters on the report sheet as the height of the graduated cylinder.

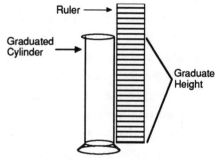

8. Repeat the experiment from **Step 1**. Use a fresh, newly weighed ball of steel wool; however, you *may* use the acetic acid left in the 50 mL beaker from before to acid rinse the steel wool. Record all of your data on the report sheet for the second run.

Figure 5.3. *Measuring the total height of the graduated cylinder.*

Report Sheet—Experiment 5
O$_2$ Content of Air

Date _____   **Section number** _____   **Name** _____

1. Data table

	Run # 1	Run # 2
Mass of Steel Wool + Paper		
Mass of Paper		
Mass of Steel Wool		
Height of Graduated Cylinder (mm)		
Final Height of Water in Graduated Cylinder (mm)		
Initial Height of Water		
Average % Oxygen Content in Air		%

2. Calculations

	Run #1	Run #2

a) Height of graduated cylinder
(from data table)   _____ mm   _____ mm.

b) Calculate the change in height of the column of water
during the experiment
(subtract the initial ruler reading
from the final ruler reading)   _____ mm   _____ mm.

c) Calculate the percentage of oxygen in air
(subtract 2(b) from 2(a), divide the result by 2(a)
minus initial height and then multiple by 100)   _____ % O$_2$ _____ % O$_2$.

d) Record the average of these two percentages
on the data table above.

Questions—Experiment 5
O$_2$ Content of Air

Date _____   Section number _____   Name _____

1. The percentage of oxygen in the air at sea level is approximately 20.6%. Calculate the percent error for your experiment by

  subtracting your average experimental % O$_2$ from 20.6 (experimental - accepted value = difference)

  dividing this result by 20.6 and then multiplying by 100 ((difference / 20.6) X 100)

2. What is a catalyst? Are there any catalysts used in this experiment? If so, what are they?

Think, Speculate, Reflect, and Ponder

3. The oxygen content of the atmosphere has a very important effect on forest and prairie fires. What would you expect might happen to the severity and number of fires on the earth if the oxygen content of the atmosphere (near the surface) increased from approximately 20.6 % to 25 %? Conversely what would you expect might happen if the natural atmospheric oxygen content became 15 %?

4. Catalytic converters are installed in all automobiles sold in the United States. These devices are placed "in-line" in the exhaust pipe, and all gases that are exhausted by the engine pass through the catalytic converter. What might the job of this device be?

5. Could a mouse live by breathing the gases left in the graduated cylinder at the end of the experiment? Explain you answer for credit.

Experiment

6

Chromatography of Natural Pigments

Samples From Home

Bring about 50 grams (2 ounces) of recently unfrozen or fresh spinach that has been torn into small pieces and sealed in a plastic bag.

Objectives

This experiment will introduce you to column chromatography and the separation of a few of the natural pigments contained in spinach.

Background

The dark green color of spinach is actually a combination of many naturally colored substances. This includes ß-carotene, which is one of many ingredients in spinach beneficial to humans. This chemical is considered a vitamin A precursor because it is converted into vitamin A in our bodies. ß-carotene is so successful as a natural color additive that the American food industry has adopted it as a dye for producing various shades of red and yellow in foods. This in turn is beneficial to consumers because it eliminates the need for a truly artificial color.

When isolated from a solution of petroleum ether, ß-carotene's crystals are red; however, when still dissolved in dilute solutions of this solvent, it exhibits a yellow color. ß-carotene is one of the natural pigments that you will isolate from spinach in this experiment. You will examine the color of this substance (while it is dissolved in a solvent) using your eye and an instrument called a spectrophotometer.

Other colored components of spinach include a group of molecules called chlorophylls, and the second component that will be separated in this experiment is a mixture of these compounds. Chlorophylls are organic molecules that coordinate (hold on to) magnesium in the center of a relatively complex ring system. Besides the important part chlorophylls play in the photosynthetic cycle of green plants, they are also extracted from plants and used to dye leather and as deodorants; however, their deodorant ability apparently has little effect on spinach.

Procedure

A. *Chromatographic separation of β-carotene and chlorophylls*

CAUTION: *Petroleum ether and acetone are very flammable liquids. Use caution and keep these solvents in the hood. Silica should not be breathed.*

1. Place your (now) room temperature spinach in about 50 mL of a 80:20 mixture petroleum ether/acetone in a mortar. Grind with the pestle until the liquid is dark green. Decant the solvent (separate the liquid from the solid by slowly pouring it into a beaker) and place 5 mL of this extract in a test tube and centrifuge for 2 minutes. (Check with the lab instructor as to the size test tube that fits your centrifuge. Measure the 5 mL using a small graduated cylinder. If you have not been instructed in the use of the centrifuge then ask the lab instructor to demonstrate. Remember to use a counterweight tube for proper balance in the centrifuge. Set the centrifuged liquid aside for **Step 6**.

Put 50 mL of petroleum ether and 50 mL of acetone from the stock containers into two separate 100 mL beakers. You can use the markings on the beakers to get the correct volumes.

2. Secure a disposable Pasture pipet in a buret clamp attached to a ring stand, taking care not to clamp and break the fragile tip of the capillary. Use a rubber band if necessary.

3. Soak a swab of glass wool (balled up to be about the diameter of a dime) in petroleum ether and then, with a piece of wire, push the wool through the top of pipet down to the beginning of the tip of the Pasteur pipet, just where the body of the pipet starts to narrow. See **Figure 6.1**. Put enough sand in the pipet secured to the ring stand to make a layer about 0.25 cm over the glass wool.

4. Add silica to this chromatographic column with a spatula until you have a layer about 5 cm high. This can best be accomplished by attaching a 1 inch piece of rubber tubing to the top of the pipet and a plastic funnel. Add the silica slowly into the funnel and tap it gently to help prevent clogging. *Take precaution when handling silica. Do not breathe this solid!* Above the 5 cm (2 inches) column of silica, place another 0.25 cm (1/8 inch) layer of sand, again using the funnel set-up. Fill the column with petroleum ether using a Pasteur pipet. At this point the column should drip at about 1 drop per second. If the dripping rate is unsatisfactory (3 drops per second is probably too fast and 1 drop every 5 seconds is too slow), stop, empty the solid material into an appropriate waste beaker and construct another column starting at **Step 2**.

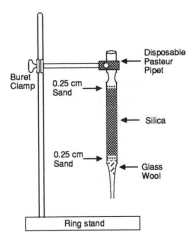

Figure 6.1. *Chromatographic column.*

5. Allow the chromatographic column to drip petroleum ether until the solvent level drops down to the top of the upper sand layer but no farther. Collect all of the waste in this experiment in a 250 or 150 mL beaker and, at the end of the lab, empty it into a suitable wastecrock or class waste container.

6. Quickly add enough spinach extract to fill the column to the top of the pipet.

7. Allow the column to drip until the spinach extract level falls to the top of the upper layer of sand. At this point fill the column again with **petroleum ether** (not more spinach extract) and keep the level of this solvent above the upper sand level throughout the steps described below. Watch carefully so that the solvent level never drops below the top–most sand layer.

8. Observe the chromatographic column. Two colored bands will separate from the original green spinach mixture. As the lower, yellow band moves downward and then exits the tip of the column, collect this fraction in a 100 mm (4 inch) test tube. You can use a small beaker if you wish. This yellow band is ß-carotene. When the petroleum ether level drops down to the upper sand layer and **after the yellow fraction has been collected**, fill the column to the top with **acetone** instead of petroleum ether as before. Continue replacing the solvent at the top of the column with acetone until the green band has eluted and been collected in another similar test tube or small beaker. The green band is the chlorophyll fraction.

B. *Spectrometric determination of ß-carotene and chlorophylls*

1. Turn on the spectrophotometer and let it warm up. Put about 4 mL of the yellow fraction that you collected in the procedure above in one of the test tube-like cuvettes that come with the spectrophotometer. (If you don't have enough, pool multiple fractions from different students.) This is the ß-carotene *sample*. Always wipe of your newly filled cuvettes with a Kim-Wipe. Put about 4 mL of petroleum ether in another cuvette. This is the *blank*. Adjust the spectrophotometer's zero knob until the meter reads 0 transmission. Place the cuvette containing the blank in the observation cell of the spectrophotometer. Make sure that the line on the cuvette always faces the same direction when you put the cuvette in the cell. Close the cover.

2. Set the wavelength dial to 700 nanometers, nm (or 7000 mµ, millimicrons). Adjust the transmittance/absorbance dial so that the meter shows 100% transmittance.

3. Remove the blank and insert the sample tube into the observation cell. Again make sure that the line faces the correct direction. Close the cover. Read the absorbance off the meter with your sample in the cell. Get your lab instructor to help you estimate the last digit correctly. Record this absorbance on the report sheet adjacent to the correct wavelength settings.

4. Remove the sample cuvette and replace it with the blank cuvette. Adjust the wavelength dial to read 690 nanometers and adjust the transmittance dial to read 100% transmittance on the meter. Remove the blank cuvette, and again replace it with the sample cuvette, taking care to adjust the position of the line as before. Read the sample absorbance from the meter with the correct accuracy and record this value.

5. Repeat this process for successively smaller wavelengths, decreasing (decrementing) the wavelength by 10 nanometers each time and ending at 400 nanometers. Don't mix up the sample and blank cuvettes or readings. If one person exchanges the samples and another person records the values, fewer mistakes will occur. Readings taken by a team can be shared on two different report sheets.

6. Repeat this procedure for the green chlorophyll fraction, **except put acetone in the blank cuvette instead of petroleum ether**. Start at 700 nm and decrement 10 nm a time down to 400 nm. Record the data on the data sheet in the correct column.

7. Graph the data for both fractions on the two different pieces of graph paper provided in this lab: The X-axis has already been numbered from 400 to 700 nanometers; number the Y-axis with numbers starting just below the lowest absorbance reading that you took and ending just above your highest absorbance reading divided evenly. After numbering your graph, plot the data by putting a dot on the graph at the intersection of the wavelength and absorbance readings. Repeat this procedure for the chlorophylls data.

For the ß-carotene graph join the dots together by a straight line between each dot. This will yield a rough example of an absorption spectrum that could be obtained with a scanning spectrophotometer (an instrument the does the wavelength decrementing automatically). The shape of this spectrum is characteristic of ß-carotene in petroleum ether solution and would be similar no matter which instrument is used to take the spectrum. This fingerprint can be useful for identification purposes.

Report Sheet—Experiment 6
Chromatography of Natural Colors

Date _____   **Section number** _____   **Name** _____

Record the absorption readings on the same line as the wavelength.

Wavelength (in nanometers)	Absorption for ß-carotene	Absorption for chlorophyll
700	_____	_____
690	_____	_____
680	_____	_____
670	_____	_____
660	_____	_____
650	_____	_____
640	_____	_____
630	_____	_____
620	_____	_____
610	_____	_____
600	_____	_____
590	_____	_____
580	_____	_____
570	_____	_____
560	_____	_____
550	_____	_____
540	_____	_____
530	_____	_____
520	_____	_____
510	_____	_____
500	_____	_____
490	_____	_____
480	_____	_____
470	_____	_____
460	_____	_____
450	_____	_____
440	_____	_____
430	_____	_____
420	_____	_____
410	_____	_____
400	_____	_____

Date _____   Section number _____   Name _____

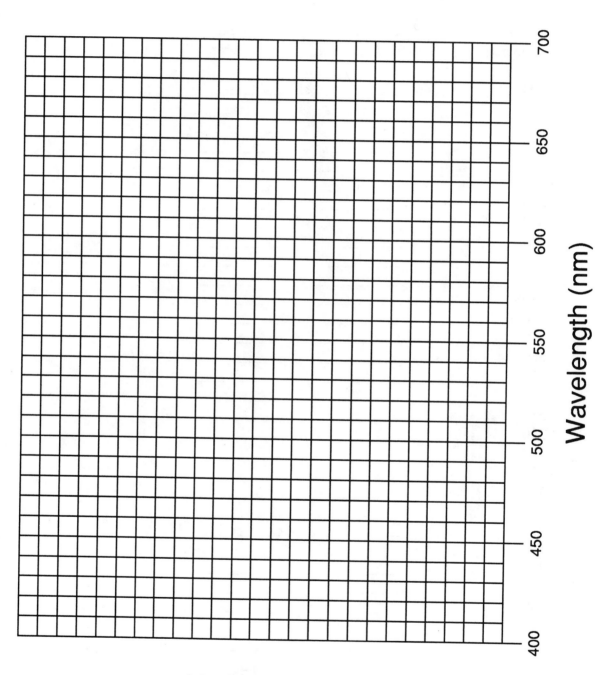

Wavelength (nm)

Absorbance

Report Sheet—Experiment 6
Chromatography of Natural Colors

Date _____   Section number _____   Name _____

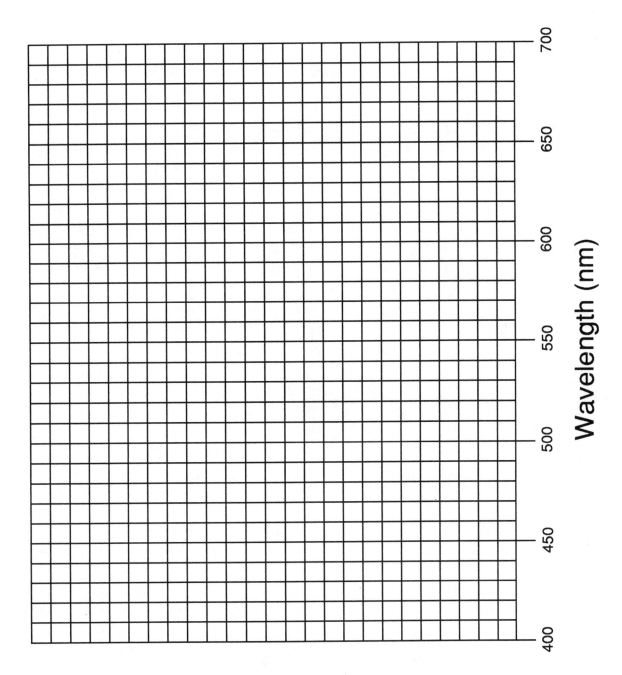

Wavelength (nm)

Absorbance

Questions—Experiment 6
Chromatography of Natural Colors

Date _____   Section number _____   Name _____

1. Why do many people consider that naturally derived dyes or pigments are safer for human beings than synthetically derived dyes when used to color food?

2. What would happen if only naturally derived dyes were allowed to be used in food sold in the United States? How would this affect the prices of foods with dyes in them?

3. Which solvent is more polar, acetone or petroleum ether? Why?

4. What would happen if acetone were the first solvent used to elute the dyes instead of petroleum ether?

5. Why is the green band referred to as chlorophylls instead of just chlorophyll?

Think, Speculate, Reflect, and Ponder

6. Can you tell the color of ß-carotene by looking at your plot of absorbance versus wavelength for your ß-carotene fraction? How?

7. Can you relate the relative polarity of acetone and water to the structures found in a reference like *The Merck Index* or *CRC Handbook of Chemistry and Physics*? How?

Experiment

7

Heat of Combustion

Sample From Home

No sample from home is required for this experiment.

Objectives

In this experiment you will determine the heat of combustion of three fuels through the experimental technique called calorimetry. Based on your results, you will calculate which of these fuels is the most energy efficient.

Background

In the burning of hydrocarbons (combustion), carbon combines with gaseous oxygen (O_2) to form carbon dioxide and hydrogen combines with O_2 to form water. The overall reaction releases chemical energy as heat. This heat is used to generate electricity, heat buildings, power automobiles or Bunsen burners, and a host of other jobs.

In 1991, coal accounted for approximately 50% of the fuel used in the United States; methane (natural gas) and nuclear power plants play a somewhat smaller role as energy sources. Cleaner energy producers such as hydrothermal, solar, and wind powered generators also contributed in a small but growing way to how Americans supply their increasing thirst for energy. In the Third World, a much larger fraction of the fuel burned is wood or charcoal (charred wood) because these are the only sources readily available. The availability of these sources is shrinking, however, as the population of the underdeveloped nations continues to increase. One of the most difficult jobs in the next century will be supplying energy to the growing populations of the world in such a way that the polluting mistakes of the past are not repeated.

An important property of any fuel is its **heat of combustion** or the amount of energy released for every gram or mole (chemical unit defining a certain number of molecules) of fuel burned. The heat of combustion determines, in part, the value of a fuel to the user. Other important factors include how efficiently (cleanly) the fuel burns and how convenient the fuel is to store, transport, and introduce into the combustion chamber of the device in which it will be burned. These aspects of fuel—heat of combustion, burning characteristics, and "storeability"—make it very important to examine the range of fuels that are available for use on our planet and to choose those that have other desirable characteristics besides merely the availability and the present market cost.

Calorimetry is the measurement of the heat released (or absorbed) in a chemical reaction. Heat generated by the burning of a fuel is captured by an instrument called a calorimeter and the amount of this energy is measured. With your calorimeter, you will determine the amount of heat released from burning a particular fuel by measuring the temperature increase of a known mass of water when it is heated by the burning fuel. The amount of temperature increase will depend on the specific heat of water, the specific heat of the flask containing it, and the heat of combustion of the fuel. The **specific heat** of a substance is the amount of heat it takes to raise the temperature of one **gram** of that substance by one degree Celsius. For example, the specific heat of water is 1 calorie per gram per degree Celsius (1 cal/g-° C): It takes 1 calorie of energy to raise the temperature of one gram of water by one degree Celsius. More water (more grams) or more temperature increase would require more energy (more calories). The specific heat defines how readily a substance soaks up and stores heat; it is a characteristic physical property of a substance, just like the melting point.

The specific heat of the pyrex glass making up the Erlenmeyer flask holding the water is much less than that of water: 0.205 cal/g-° C. Therefore, it takes less energy to raise the temperature of the flask 1 degree than it does to raise the temperature of the same mass of water by one degree. When you perform this experiment, the energy released by burning the fuel will heat both the water and the flask containing that water (we assume by the same amount) so both the specific heat of water and the specific heat of the flask must be taken into account.

Procedure

A. *Heat of combustion of methanol*

1. Weigh a clean and dry 250 mL Erlenmeyer flask to 0.01 g and record this mass on the report sheet.

2. With the flask still on the balance pan, add tap water to the flask until the balance reads about 200 g of <u>added</u> mass. Record the exact mass of the flask plus the water on your report sheet in the appropriate blank. By subtracting the datum from **Step 1** from that in **Step 2** you can determine the exact mass of water that you added to the flask. Record this mass, obtained by subtraction, in the correct place on the report sheet.

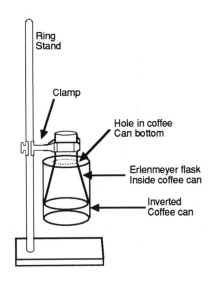

3. Set up your calorimeter by carefully inserting the flask containing the water through the hole in the coffee can bottom and securing the flask to the ring stand with a clamp (refer to **Figure 7.1**). Be careful of the sharp edges of the cut out metal bottom! The can will completely cover the lower part of the flask with about an inch to spare.

4. Put a small piece of rubber tubing over the tip of your thermometer's bulb to protect it during stirring.

Figure 7.1. *Calorimeter apparatus.*

5. Place 20 to 30 mL of methanol in your alcohol burner. Don't pull the wick up out of the wick holder any more than it already is! Your lab instructor has adjusted the wick already for the best flame height.

6. Place the cap on the alcohol burner and weigh to 0.01g. Record this mass on your report sheet.

7. Record the starting temperature of the water in the Erlenmeyer to the nearest 0.1 ° C. The thermometer will now remain in the water in the flask for the remainder of the experiment.

8. Place the burner beneath the Erlenmeyer flask making sure that the coffee can will at least cover the flame during the experiment. Remember the idea is to catch <u>all the heat that you can from the burning flame</u>; however, if you lower the can/flask too much it will smother the flame.

9. Light the alcohol burner with a match.

10. As you heat, continually stir the water with the thermometer until a 20 °C change in temperature has occurred as measured by the thermometer in the water. You can monitor the flame by watching its reflection in the neck of the flask. If the flame goes out quickly relight it with another match.

11. After the temperature has risen by 20 °C, blow out the flame and continue to stir and measure the temperature until it stops rising. Record the maximum temperature. This may take 20 or 30 seconds after you blow out the flame.

12. Remove the burner from under the coffee can and reweigh it with its cap on. Record the weight to 0.01g.

13. You now have recorded on your report sheet the mass of water that you heated, the temperature increase of that water, and the mass of fuel it took to cause this increase.

14. Repeat **Steps 1** through **12.**

B. *Heat of combustion of candle wax*

1. Exactly as before, weigh a dry Erlenmeyer flask (record this mass), add approximately 200 g water, and determine the weight of the water that you added to 0.01 g. Again, you will have to subtract the mass of the empty flask from the mass of the flask plus water. Reassemble the calorimeter as before being careful not to cut yourself on the sharp metal edges!

2. Get a candle from the stock room or supply cart. Light the candle and drip hot wax onto the center of the watch glass until the bottom of the candle can be stuck securely to the watch glass. Blow out the candle and allow it to cool and the wax to harden.

3. Weigh the watch glass and candle to 0.01g. Record this mass.

4. Record the starting temperature of the water.

5. Position the candle under the coffee can as before and light the candle. Make sure that the candle's flame is not snuffed out by the bottom of the flask.

6. Stirring continuously and exactly as before, heat the water in the flask until a 20 °C temperature rise has occurred. Record the highest temperature achieved by the water after you blow out the candle.

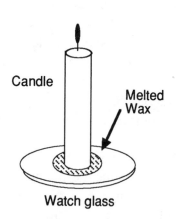

Figure 7.2. *Candle setup.*

7. Reweigh the candle and watch glass to 0.01g and record this mass.

8. You now have recorded on your report sheet the mass of water heated, its increase in temperature, and the mass of candle that was needed to cause this rise.

9. Repeat **Steps 1** through **7**.

C. *Heat of combustion of wood*

1. Repeat the apparatus assembly. Make sure that you get the weight of the clean and dry Erlenmeyer first. Then get the weight of this flask containing approximately 200 grams of water exactly as before. Record these masses as well as the calculated mass of the added water.

2. Get 20 wooden splints from the stock room or supply cart.

3. Put the splints on top of a wooden block and weigh the splints and the block to 0.01 grams.

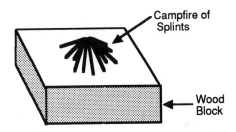

4. Carefully arrange the splints in a 5 or 6 level campfire (or stacked like a log cabin) on top of the wooden block so that when lit, as many of the splints will burn as possible.

Figure 7.3 *"Campfire" of wooden splints.*

5. Record the temperature of the water to 0.1° C

6. Place the splint campfire underneath the coffee can. You may need to raise the flask/can assembly by moving the clamp up the ring stand. Don't forget to retighten the clamp after you move it. After the fire is lit, carefully reposition the calorimeter so that as much of the wooden block and the campfire is covered as possible.

7. Light the campfire in numerous places using a wooden match, allowing the fire to burn toward the middle. Relight the fire if necessary. You may have to adjust the coffee can's height to be able to get to the edges of the campfire with your match.

8. Constantly stirring the water with the thermometer, record the highest temperature that the water temperature rises to <u>after the wood fire burns out</u>. Note: If the fire burns too slowly or too quickly the experimental results will have a large error. You may have to experiment with the configuration of your campfire to get it to burn in such a way that lots of the heat doesn't escape the confines of your calorimeter. Watch how other students in your lab design their campfires and adopt the best configuration. Hint: If you see lots of soot on the outside of your coffee can, your campfire probably burned too quickly.

9. After the fire has burned out, reweigh the wooden block and (burned splints) to 0.01 gram. Take care not to spill or lose any of the burned residue. Put any pieces that fall off of the block back on the block before you reweigh.

10. You now have recorded on your report sheet the mass of water, the temperature increase, and the mass of wood necessary to cause this temperature rise.

11. Repeat **Steps 1** through **9**.

Report Sheet—Experiment 7
Heat of Combustion

Date _____   Section number _____   Name _____

Fuel ------>	Methanol	Methanol	Candle	Candle	Wood	Wood
Trial # ------>	# 1	# 2	# 1	# 2	# 1	# 2
Mass of Flask + water						
Mass of empty flask						
Mass of water						
Final water temperature						
Initial water temperature						
Temp. change						
Initial mass of burner + cap						
Final mass of burner + cap						
Mass of methanol burned						
Initial mass candle + watch glass						
Final mass candle + watch glass						
Mass of candle burned						
Initial mass wooden block + splints						
Final mass block + burned splints						
Mass of wood burned						

Average Heat of Combustion	cal/gram		cal/gram		cal/gram	

Calculations

A. *Heat of combustion of methanol*

The amount of heat absorbed by the calorimeter (Erlenmeyer + water) when methanol was burned may be calculated from the masses of the Erlenmeyer and water, the temperature change, and the respective specific heats. Repeat the calculation for each trial separately and then average the heat of combustion for each trial at the end. Remember that for a particular trial, the temperature change for the flask will be the same as the temperature change for the water.

Heat absorbed by Erlenmeyer flask (in calories) = (mass of Erlenmeyer) X (0.205 cal/g-°C) X (temperature change):

Mass of empty flask	_____g trial 1.
	_____g trial 2.
Temperature change	_____° C trial 1.
	_____° C trial 2.
Specific heat of pyrex glass	0.205 cal/g-° C
Heat absorbed by Erlenmeyer flask	_____calories trial 1.
	_____calories trial 2.

Heat absorbed by water (in calories) = (mass of water) X (1 cal/g-°C) X (temperature change):

Mass of water	_____g trial 1.
	_____g trial 2.
Temperature change	_____° C trial 1.
	_____° C trial 2.
Specific heat of water	1 cal/g-° C
Heat absorbed by water	_____calories trial 1.
	_____calories trial 2.

Total heat absorbed by calorimeter = Heat absorbed by Erlenmeyer flask + Heat absorbed by water

	_____ calories trial 1.
	_____ calories trial 2.

Heat of combustion of methanol = heat absorbed by calorimeter divided by the mass of methanol burned

Mass of methanol burned

_____grams trial 1.
_____grams trial 2.

Heat of Combustion

_____calories/gram trial 1.
_____calories/gram trial 2.

Average heat of combustion for methanol

_____calories/gram.
(record on Report Sheet)

B. *Heat of combustion of candle wax*

The amount of heat absorbed by the calorimeter (Erlenmeyer + water) when candle wax was burned may be calculated from the masses of the Erlenmeyer and water, the temperature change, and the respective specific heats.

Heat absorbed by Erlenmeyer flask (in calories) = (mass of Erlenmeyer) X (0.205 cal/g-°C) X (temperature change):

Mass of flask

_____g trial 1.
_____g trial 2.

Temperature change

_____° C trial 1.
_____° C trial 2.

Specific heat of pyrex glass

0.205 cal/g-°C

Heat absorbed by Erlenmeyer flask

_____calories trial 1.
_____calories trial 2.

Heat absorbed by water (in calories) = (mass of water) X (1 cal/g-°C) X (temperature change):

Mass of water

_____g trial 1.
_____g trial 2.

Temperature change

_____° C trial 1.
_____° C trial 2.

Specific heat of water

1 cal/g-°C

Heat absorbed by water

_____calories trial 1.
_____calories trial 2.

Total heat absorbed by calorimeter = Heat absorbed by Erlenmeyer flask + Heat absorbed by water

_____calories trial 1.
_____calories trial 2.

Heat of combustion of candle wax = heat absorbed by calorimeter divided by the mass of candle burned

_____calories/gram trial 1.
_____calories/gram trial 2.

Average heat of combustion of candle wax

_____calories/gram.
(record on Report Sheet)

C. *Heat of combustion of wood*

The amount of heat absorbed by the calorimeter (Erlenmeyer + water) when wood was burned may be calculated from the masses of the Erlenmeyer and water, the temperature change, and the respective specific heats.

Heat absorbed by Erlenmeyer flask (in calories) = (mass of Erlenmeyer) X (0.205 cal/g-°C) X (temperature change):

Mass of flask

_____g trial 1.
_____g trial 2.

Temperature change

_____° C trial 1.
_____° C trial 2.

Specific heat of pyrex glass

0.205 cal/g-°C

Heat absorbed by flask

_____calories trial 1.
_____calories trial 2.

Heat absorbed by water (in calories) = (mass of water) X (1 cal/g-°C) X (temperature change):

Mass of water

_____g trial 1.
_____g trial 2.

Temperature change

_____° C trial 1.
_____° C trial 2.

Specific heat of water

1 cal/g-°C

Heat absorbed by water   _____calories trial 1.

_____calories trial 2.

Total heat absorbed by calorimeter = Heat absorbed by flask + Heat absorbed by water

_____ calories trial 1.

_____ calories trial 2.

Heat of combustion of wood = heat absorbed by calorimeter divided by the mass of wood burned

_____calories/gram trial 1.

_____calories/gram trial 2.

Average heat of combustion of wood   _____calories/gram.

(record on Report Sheet)

Questions—Experiment 7
Heat of Combustion

Date _____   Section number _____   Name _____

1. Which of the three fuels you used yields the most energy per gram?

2. Number the following substances in order of increasing specific heats:
Aluminum, Argon, Beryllium, Copper, Helium, Hydrogen, Lead, and Xenon
You will need specific heat data for this problem from a reference like the *CRC Handbook of Chemistry and Physics.*

3. What other factors besides energy released per gram of fuel determine the usefulness of a fuel?

4. What might be the largest source of error in this experiment?

Think, Speculate, Reflect, and Ponder

5. Are there any environmental factors that are taken into account when choosing a fuel? If so what are they and why should they be taken into account when choosing a fuel?

6. Calculate the heat of combustion of methanol on a per mole basis assuming methanol has a molecular weight of 32.05 grams/mole.

7. Why do you have to calculate the heats of combustion of wood and the candle on a per gram basis instead of a per mole basis?

Experiment

8

Unknowns in an Homologous Series

Samples From Home

No sample from home is required for this experiment.

Objectives

Using calorimetry, this experiment will allow you to compare the different potential energies of a family of fuels that structurally vary only in carbon chain length: Each member of the family of alcohols that you will study is identical except for the number of CH_2 units it contains. The relationship between carbon number and heat of combustion will allow you to determine the identity of an unknown member of the series.

Background

In a sense, all of the energy sources that we use on earth are derived from solar energy. Even the radioactive elements that fuel nuclear power plants ultimately came from stars. Energy from the sun in the form of light is captured by plants by the formation of chemical bonds. Later these bonds are broken and their energy is released in the form of chemical or heat energy (this is called cellular respiration).

The process of combustion (or burning) is similar to respiration in that high energy, less stable molecules react and form lower energy, more stable products, thereby giving up energy that can be used for some purpose. Wood, containing stored energy, burns in the presence of oxygen, and the results are lower energy, more stable products plus heat given off. This is, of course, true for all fossil fuels such as methane, coal, and petroleum. In the case of most combustion, human beings are interested in capturing the energy derived from the burning of the fuel in order to do something useful such as powering an automobile or heating a home. In the case of cellular respiration, organisms are "interested" in powering the processes necessary for life: reproduction, growth, movement, etc. All fuels are not equivalent, however. Experiment 7, *Heat of Combustion* compared the energy contained in three fuels that were decidedly unequal in the amount of energy that each supplied per gram (differing heat contents). The differences in these three fuels are in great part due to their differing chemical structures.

Methane (CH_4), ethane (CH_3-CH_3), and propane (CH_3-CH_2-CH_3) are homologues (also spelled homologs). This means that they differ from each other only in the number of CH_2 groups they contain. In this experiment, a series of homologues will be burned, the energy that is released captured, and the heats of combustion of each compound measured. You will be able to determine the structure of an unknown member of this group by comparing its heat of combustion to the heats of combustion of other, known members of the series.

The workhorse in this experiment will be your alcohol burner. The fuels that you will examine are all alcohols (they contain a single -OH group). You will use your burner to study four different alcohols over the course of the experiment, each time using a different wick that is specified for each fuel. It is very important that wicks saturated with one fuel not be used with other fuels. This will yield an unacceptable error in the heat of combustion that you determine because the wicks retain a relatively large amount of fuel from the last burner they were in. To make sure that we avoid this problem, wicks that have been used in methanol (an alcohol containing 1 carbon atom) will be deposited into a beaker labelled METHANOL WICKS; wicks that have been used with unknown #1 will be deposited in a beaker labelled UNKNOWN #1 WICKS, propanol (an alcohol containing 3 carbon atoms) wicks in a beaker labelled PROPANOL WICKS, etc. If you need a wick for a pentanol run (pentanol is an alcohol containing 5 carbon atoms), take out the wick that is in your burner and put it in the correctly labelled beaker and get a pentanol wick from the PENTANOL wick beaker.

When you are inserting a new wick into the wick holder of the alcohol burner, insert the new wick *up from the bottom* and do not pull the wick more that a few millimeters above the top of the wick holder. If you do extend the wick too much, your flame will be too tall and this will cause an error in your results because you will lose too much heat during the experiment, *heat that you want to catch with your calorimeter*! Please ask your lab instructor if you have a question about the heights of your wicks.

Since you will be emptying and adding different alcohols to your burner, it is important that you empty the burner of the first fuel as completely as possible before you add the next fuel. Pour the leftover fuel from your alcohol burner into the bottle containing the fuel with the correct name: The bottle labelled PENTANOL FUEL will contain only leftover pentanol; the bottle labelled UNKNOWN ALCOHOL # 2 will contain only leftover unknown alcohol #2, etc. Be careful when you empty and refill your burner so the beakers will only have the correct fuels in them.

Similarly, when it is time to put a new fuel in your burner make sure that you "fuel-up" from the bottle containing the correct fuel. If you have any question about which wick beaker or fuel bottle is which, ask your lab instructor. Finally, it is not necessary to completely fill your burner with fuel. Only 20 to 30 mL of fuel is necessary for two trials with each fuel.

Procedure

The procedures and calculations for this experiment are identical to those of the last calorimeter experiment. Reviewing the introduction to that experiment will help you with this one.

A. *Heat of Combustion of Methanol*

1. Weigh a clean and dry 250 mL Erlenmeyer flask to 0.01 g and record this mass on the report sheet.

2. With the flask still on the balance pan, add tap water to the flask until the balance reads about 200 g of *added* mass. Record the exact mass of the flask plus the water on your report sheet in the appropriate blank. By subtracting the datum from **Step 1** from that in **Step 2** you can determine the exact mass of water that you added to the flask. Record this mass, obtained by subtraction, in the correct place on the report sheet.

3. Set up your calorimeter by carefully inserting the flask containing the water through the hole in the coffee can bottom and securing the flask to the ring stand with a clamp (refer to Figure 8.1). Be careful of the sharp edges of the cut out metal bottom! The can will completely cover the lower part of the flask with about an inch to spare.

4. Put a small piece of rubber tubing over the tip of your thermometer's bulb to protect it during stirring.

5. Place 20 to 30 mL of methanol in your alcohol burner. Don't pull the wick up out of the wick holder any more than it already is! Your lab instructor has adjusted the wick already for the best flame height.

6. Place the cap on the alcohol burner and weigh to 0.01g. Record this mass on your report sheet.

7. Record the starting temperature of the water in the Erlenmeyer to the nearest 0.1 ° C. The thermometer will now remain in the water in the flask for the rest of the experiment.

8. Place the burner beneath the Erlenmeyer flask making sure that the coffee can will at least cover the flame during the experiment. Remember the idea is to catch *all the heat that you can from the burning flame*; however, if you lower the can/flask too much it will smother the flame.

9. Light the alcohol burner with a match.

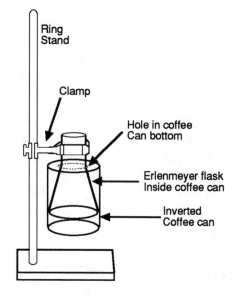

Figure 8.1. *Calorimeter apparatus.*

10. As you heat, continually stir the water with the thermometer until approximately 20 ° C change in temperature has occurred as measured by the thermometer in the water. You can monitor the flame by watching its reflection in the neck of the flask. If the flame goes out quickly relight it with another match.

11. After the temperature has risen by 20 ° C, blow out the flame and continue to stir and measure the temperature until it stops rising. Record the maximum temperature. This may take 20 or 30 seconds after you blow out the flame.

12. Remove the burner from under the coffee can and reweigh it with its cap on. Record the weight to 0.01g.

13. Repeat **Steps 1** through **12** without adding any more fuel. You will need to start **Step 1** with a dry, room temperature flask into which you add tap water.

B. *Heat of Combustion of Propanol*

Repeat Procedure **A** *with propanol instead of methanol as the fuel.* Make sure that when you are emptying and replacing the fuel in your burner you use the correct wick beaker and fuel bottle: Place the old wick in the beaker labelled METHANOL WICKS and pour any leftover methanol in the bottle labelled METHANOL FUEL. Refill your burner with propanol from the bottle labelled PROPANOL FUEL and position a wick from the beaker labelled PROPANOL WICKS in your wick holder. Perform two trials with this fuel and record your data on the report sheet.

C. *Heat of Combustion of Pentanol*

Repeat Procedure **A** with pentanol. Make sure when you are emptying and replacing the fuel in your burner that you use the correct wick beaker and fuel bottle. Also, do the experiment in duplicate (two trials) as before.

D. *Heat of Combustion of an Unknown*

Choose one or the other of the unknowns and repeat the procedure in procedure **A** (in duplicate) with the unknown alcohol as your fuel. (Your lab instructor may prefer to assign unknowns.) Don't forget to record your unknown number on the report sheet. When you finish, you will have two trials for each of the known alcohols and one of the unknown alcohols.

Calculations

A. *Calculating the Heats of Combustion*

The amount of heat absorbed by the calorimeter (Erlenmeyer + water) when each fuel was burned may be calculated from the masses of the Erlenmeyer and water, the temperature change, and the respective specific heats. The specific heat of a material is characteristic of that material and is the amount of heat necessary to raise the temperature of 1 gram of the material by 1 degree (cal/g-°C). Repeat the calculation for each fuel for each trial separately and then average the heat of combustion for each trial at the end. Remember that for a particular trial, the temperature change for the flask will be the same as the temperature change for the water.

Heat of combustion for methanol

Heat absorbed by Erlenmeyer flask (in calories)
(multiply the mass of the Erlenmeyer times 0.205 cal/g-°C then multiply the result by the temperature change):

Mass of empty flask	_____g trial 1.
	_____g trial 2.
Temperature change	_____° C trial 1.
	_____° C trial 2.
Specific heat of pyrex glass	0.205 cal/g-° C
Heat absorbed by Erlenmeyer flask	_____calories trial 1.
	_____calories trial 2.

Heat absorbed by water (in calories)
(multiply the mass of water times 1.00 cal/g-°C them multiply the result by the temperature change):

Mass of water	_____g trial 1.
	_____g trial 2.

Temperature change   _____° C trial 1.

_____° C trial 2.

Specific heat of water   1.00 cal/g-° C

Heat absorbed by water   _____calories trial 1.

_____calories trial 2.

Total heat absorbed by calorimeter
(add heat absorbed by Erlenmeyer flask and the heat absorbed by water)

_____ calories trial 1.

_____ calories trial 2.

Heat of combustion of methanol
(divide the heat absorbed by calorimeter by the mass of methanol burned)

Mass of methanol burned

_____grams trial 1.

_____grams trial 2.

Heat of combustion   _____calories/gram trial 1.

_____calories/gram trial 2.

Average heat of combustion for methanol   _____calories/gram.
(record on Report Sheet)

Heat of combustion of propanol

Heat absorbed by Erlenmeyer flask (in calories)
(multiply the mass of the Erlenmeyer times 0.205 cal/g-°C then multiply the result by the temperature change):

Mass of empty flask   _____g trial 1.

_____g trial 2.

Temperature change   _____° C trial 1.

_____° C trial 2.

Specific heat of pyrex glass   0.205 cal/g-° C

Heat absorbed by Erlenmeyer flask   _____calories trial 1.

_____calories trial 2.

Heat absorbed by water (in calories)
(multiply the mass of water times 1.00 cal/g-°C then multiply the result by the temperature change):

Mass of water

_____ g trial 1.
_____ g trial 2.

Temperature change

_____ ° C trial 1.
_____ ° C trial 2.

Specific heat of water

1.00 cal/g-° C

Heat absorbed by water

_____ calories trial 1.
_____ calories trial 2.

Total heat absorbed by calorimeter
(add the heat absorbed by Erlenmeyer flask and the heat absorbed by water

_____ calories trial 1.
_____ calories trial 2.

Heat of combustion of propanol
(divide the heat absorbed by calorimeter by the mass of propanol burned)

Mass of propanol burned

_____ grams trial 1.
_____ grams trial 2.

Heat of combustion

_____ calories/gram trial 1.
_____ calories/gram trial 2.

Average heat of combustion for propanol

_____ calories/gram.
(record on Report Sheet)

Heat of combustion of pentanol

Heat absorbed by Erlenmeyer flask (in calories)
(multiply the mass of the Erlenmeyer times 0.205 cal/g-°C then multiply the result by the temperature change):

Mass of empty flask

_____ g trial 1.
_____ g trial 2.

Temperature change   _____° C trial 1.
_____° C trial 2.

Specific heat of pyrex glass   0.205 cal/g-° C

Heat absorbed by Erlenmeyer flask   _____calories trial 1.
_____calories trial 2.

Heat absorbed by water (in calories)
(multiply the mass of the water times 1.00 cal/g-°C) then multiply the result by the temperature change):

Mass of water   _____g trial 1.
_____g trial 2.

Temperature change   _____° C trial 1.
_____° C trial 2.

Specific heat of water   1.00 cal/g-° C

Heat absorbed by water   _____calories trial 1.
_____calories trial 2.

Total heat absorbed by calorimeter
(add the heat absorbed by Erlenmeyer flask and the heat absorbed by water)

_____ calories trial 1.
_____ calories trial 2.

Heat of combustion of pentanol
(divide the heat absorbed by calorimeter by the mass of pentanol burned)

Mass of pentanol burned

_____grams trial 1.
_____grams trial 2.

Heat of combustion   _____calories/gram trial 1.
_____calories/gram trial 2.

Average heat of combustion for pentanol   _____calories/gram.
(record on Report Sheet)

Heat of combustion of an unknown alcohol

Unknown # _____

Heat absorbed by Erlenmeyer flask (in calories)
(multiply the mass of the Erlenmeyer times 0.205 cal/g-°C then multiply the result by the temperature change):

Mass of empty flask

_____ g trial 1.
_____ g trial 2.

Temperature change

_____ ° C trial 1.
_____ ° C trial 2.

Specific heat of pyrex glass

0.205 cal/g-° C

Heat absorbed by Erlenmeyer flask

_____ calories trial 1.
_____ calories trial 2.

Heat absorbed by water (in calories)
(multiply the mass of the water times 1.00 cal/g-°C then multiply the result by the temperature change):

Mass of water

_____ g trial 1.
_____ g trial 2.

Temperature change

_____ ° C trial 1.
_____ ° C trial 2.

Specific heat of water

1.00 cal/g-° C

Heat absorbed by water

_____ calories trial 1.
_____ calories trial 2.

Total heat absorbed by calorimeter
(add the heat absorbed by the Erlenmeyer flask and the heat absorbed by water)

_____ calories trial 1.
_____ calories trial 2.

Heat of combustion of unknown
(divide the heat absorbed by calorimeter by the mass of unknown alcohol burned)

Mass of unknown burned

_____grams trial 1.
_____grams trial 2.

Heat of combustion

_____calories/gram trial 1.
_____calories/gram trial 2.

Average heat of combustion for unknown alcohol

_____calories/gram.
(record on Report Sheet)

B. *Calibration Plot: Heat of Combustion per Gram Versus Carbon Number*

On the graph paper provided, make a calibration plot of the heat of combustion of each of the known alcohols (in calories/gram) versus the number of carbons that each alcohol molecule contains (see below). Put the number of carbons on the x-axis and the heat of combustion per gram on the y-axis. For example, number your x-axis from 0 to 6 (carbons) and number your y-axis from 0 to 10,000 (calories per gram). Your experimental data points will fit on this graph as described.

Methanol's structure is CH_3OH; it has one carbon per molecule. Propanol's structure is $CH_3CH_2CH_2OH$; it has 3 carbons. Pentanol's structure is $CH_3CH_2CH_2CH_2CH_2OH$, and it has 5 carbons per molecule. Your calibration plot of heat of combustion per gram versus the number of carbons in a molecule of the fuel will have three points: one for methanol, one for propanol, and one for pentanol.

Draw a straight line that visually best approximates the lie of these three points. If done well this line will be equidistant from all three of your points. *The best fit line will not pass through the intersection of the x-and y-axes.* You can place a long pencil or a ruler down on the graph and move it around until it passes an equal distance from all three. Finally draw a line on the graph that fits this line.

C. *Determination of Unknown's Carbon Number*

Plot the heat of combustion per gram of your unknown alcohol on the calibration plot. Determine the number of carbons in you unknown alcohol by relating the number of carbons to the heat of combustion per gram that you calculated. Here's how: The calculated heat of combustion of your unknown will fall somewhere on the y-axis. Draw a *horizontal* line from the point on the y-axis that represents the calculated heat of combustion per gram of your unknown over to the best-fit line that you drew in the step above. Next draw a *vertical* line from that point on the best fit line down to the x-axis. This point on the x-axis should be close to the whole number of carbon atoms that your unknown alcohol contains. If this point is not exactly on a whole number then decide which whole number it lies *nearest* to on the x-axis. This is the number of carbons in your unknown alcohol. Remember: None of the number of carbons in the unknowns in this experiment is the same as any of the known alcohols. Write down the number of carbons in your unknown on the report sheet. If you have difficulty with this step, ask a classmate or your lab instructor for help.

Report Sheet—Experiment 8
Homologous Series

Date _____   Section number _____   Name _____

Fuel ------>	Methanol	Methanol	Propanol	Propanol	Pentanol	Pentanol	Your Unknown	Your Unknown
Trial # ------>	#1	#2	#1	#2	#1	#2	Trial #1	Trial #2
Mass of Flask + water								
Mass of empty flask								
Mass of water								
Final water temperature								
Initial water temperature								
Temp. change								
Heat of Combustion								
Average Heat of Combustion		cal/gram		cal/gram		cal/gram		cal/gram

Unknown number _____

Number of carbons in your unknown alcohol determined from the calibration plot _____ .

Report Sheet—Experiment 8
Homologous Series

Date _____ Section number _____ Name _____

Number of Carbons Atoms per Molecule

Heat of Combustion (cal/gram)

Questions—Experiment 8
Homologous Series

Date _____   Section number _____   Name _____

1. Could you see any visible difference between the flames of the different known alcohols? In other words, did carbon number seem to affect the colors of your flames? How?

2. If you answered yes to question 1, what would you expect the color of a flame that is burning a 10 carbon alcohol would be? If you answered no to question one, then reread the background to Experiment 1, *The Ubiquitous Bunsen Burner* and answer the following question: What effect does the ratio of the reactants mixing in the Bunsen burner's flame have upon the products of the reaction taking place?

3. What were the labels on the two axes of your graph?

Think, Speculate, Reflect, and Ponder

4. Why is the best fit line on your graph not drawn through all the points and/or why would the three experimental points that you derived from your data not always fall in a straight line?

5. Is there a way to calculate an equation that mathematically represents your best-fit line? How could you do this?

Experiment

9

Alcohol Content of Beverages
and
Consumer Products
(or How the Moonshiners Would Do It)

Samples From Home

Bring 50 mL of a liquid containing water and ethyl alcohol as the only significant volatile components, such as after shave lotion, cologne, wine, mouthwash, beer, etc. Check the label, or check with the lab instructor if in doubt. (NOTE: Cough syrup will not work, and rubbing alcohol is not the same as ethyl alcohol).

Objectives

The nature of distillation and the usefulness of a distillation apparatus for separating substances will be explored, and typical distillation behavior of two liquids illustrated. The use of a hydrometer or Westphal balance will be shown for determining the density of the distilled liquid, and the results used to verify or discover the actual alcohol content of the test sample.

Background

When relatively large amounts of liquids must be separated, purified, or analyzed, the first technique a chemist thinks of is distillation. Moonshiners know about it, and so do the "reveenoorers." All liquids which have a reasonable tendency to evaporate ("volatile" liquids as chemists would say) can be caused to boil (to "distill") if heated sufficiently under an appropriate pressure. If such a volatile liquid (like water) has mixed with it something else that is non-volatile (like salt), distillation will be able to separate the two components easily.

For example, boiling salt water will result in the volatile water coming off as steam, leaving the solid non-volatile salt residue behind. In practice, the hot liquid vapors (steam in this case) are passed through a condenser in order to cool them sufficiently so that the steam will condense back into water. No chemical change has taken place—the salt is still salt, and the water is still water. If we were to pour the water back onto the salt residue, the original salt water mixture would form.

The condenser itself simply consists of two concentric tubes—the inner one for your hot vapors to condense in, and the outer one in which to circulate cooling water. There is no opening joining the inner and outer tubes, and thus no way water can get inside of the inner tube. The liquid you will see dripping out of the end of your condenser will just be due to the hot distillate vapors condensing back into a liquid in the inner tube.

But what about using distillation to separate two liquids which have different tendencies to evaporate, that is liquids that have different boiling points? For our purposes, we need stress only this: although such separations can often (but not always) be performed, they are more difficult than it might seem. Most of the oxygen and nitrogen used in commerce and laboratories is isolated from the distillation of air—after it has first been turned into a liquid mixture containing these two elements by cooling to −196 ° C. However, using a mixture of water (boiling point 100 ° C) and alcohol (boiling point 78 ° C) as an example, heating of this solution to 78 ° C does not result in all the alcohol boiling off at this temperature. Furthermore, it is actually impossible to completely separate just pure alcohol and pure water by distillation. As is so often the case, the more we learn about a subject, the more we find we have left to learn. But the fascinating twists and turns of distillation will have to wait for your next (?) chemistry course!

The method for alcohol analysis described in this experiment is basically the same as that used in the analysis of beer and wine by official government agencies. The alcohol and water do not have to be separated from each other. The purpose of carrying out the distillation is to remove both the volatile components—the water and all the alcohol—from your sample so that the composition of this mixture may be determined. Direct composition analysis on the original sample itself would be complicated by the presence of many other unknown substances dissolved in the solution.

Since it is not practical to distill all of the liquid in your sample (you should understand this limitation better after performing the distillation yourself), some water is added to your sample before distillation, and then distillation is stopped when just this same volume of water remains in the flask. As long as the temperature on your thermometer registers close to 100° C, you should know that by then all the lower boiling alcohol has distilled over into your receiver vessel and that water is the only volatile liquid left in the flask.

There are several ways for determining the percent composition of an alcohol/water mixture. We will use one to which we already have been introduced—that of density measurement. Pure water will have a density of 1.00 g/cm³, and pure ethyl alcohol 0.798 g/cm³, at 20 ° C. Mixtures of these two liquids will have densities between these values, and by reference to tables in handbooks your measured density can be converted into per cent alcohol. The hydrometer is a device for measuring quickly such densities and is in principle the same way that your car battery fluid is checked to see if the battery is run down. The more dense a liquid is, the higher the hydrometer will float in it, and conversely, the less dense a liquid is the further down in it the hydrometer will submerge. Since all the alcohol from your sample ends up in an equal volume of distillate, the % alcohol in the distillate will equal the % alcohol in your sample.

Liquid densities can be very accurately determined using a Westphal balance. This balance measures the buoyancy of a calibrated glass "plummet" when immersed in a liquid. This buoyancy effect is dependent upon the density of the unknown liquid. The density can be read directly from the balance itself.

Procedure

Set up a distillation apparatus as diagrammed in Figure 9.1. Using clamps and ringstands as necessary, secure both the flask and the condenser. Be careful not to use undue force when inserting your thermometer, especially when using a rubber stopper. Lubricate the hole first with water or glycerine. Have your set-up checked by the lab instructor before commencing heating.

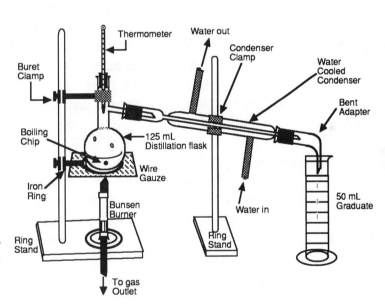

Figure 9.1. *Apparatus for simple distillation.*

1. If your sample is carbonated (beer, sparkling wines), you will need to shake it in a 500 mL Erlenmeyer flask for 5-10 minutes until "fizzing" subsides before proceeding. Remove the stopper that holds the thermometer, insert a long stem funnel in the top of the flask, pour in 50 mL of your sample to be analyzed, and follow with 25 mL of water. Remove the funnel, add a boiling chip and (if your sample was carbonated) a few drops of an antifoaming agent. Replace the stopper and thermometer.

Turn on the water so that a slow stream passes through the condenser, and commence heating the flask. Heat strongly at first until a ring of condensing vapors is seen moving up towards the thermometer. (You should also be able to feel the hot vapor ring with your fingers). Then cut back the heat with the gas supply valve and adjust so that the liquid drips into the graduated cylinder at a rate of about one drop per second.

Initially try to adjust the heat by partly closing the gas control valve to the Bunsen burner. If you still find it difficult to control the heat and hence the rate of distillation (a likely situation), slide the wire gauze in and out so as to place open screen (more heat) or white ceramic center (less heat) between the burner flame and distillation flask. By sliding this gauze around you should be able to find just the right position to give you the desired one drop per second distillation rate.

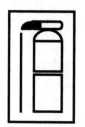

2. Note the temperatures of your distillate vapors during the course of the distillation and record your observations. By the time that you have collected 50 mL of distillate, STOP—the temperature should have risen to 98 to 100 °C. (Some samples like perfumes and mouthwashes may yield a cloudy liquid towards the end of the distillation.)

3. With the help of your lab instructor, measure the density of your liquid by either (a) using a Westphal balance, or (b) slowly lowering a hydrometer (*Fragile!*) into the liquid in your graduate. Make sure that it is not touching the bottom. Hydrometers come in different density ranges, so be very careful to read accurately and correctly the proper number off the hydrometer stem. Check with your lab instructor for help if you are in doubt. If for any reason you cannot measure the density of your liquid with a Westphal balance or hydrometer, you will have to calculate it from a measurement of the liquid weight and volume as done in Experiment 2, *Going Metric with the Rest of the World*. Note the *method* of density measurement that you used on the report sheet and record the measured density.

4. Refer to the alcohol/water density table on the next two pages and determine the alcohol content of your solution. Note on the report sheet whether the composition that you report is percent by weight or by volume (consult with the lab instructor for help in deciding which is appropriate for your sample). For our purposes, we shall consider density to be the same as the specific gravity.

Specific Gravity of Mixtures of Ethyl Alcohol and Water by Volume and by Weight[*]

Specific Gravity	% Alcohol by Volume	% Alcohol by Weight	Specific Gravity	% Alcohol by Volume	% Alcohol by Weight	Specific Gravity	% Alcohol by Volume	% Alcohol by Weight
1.00000	0.00	0.00	0.99417	4.00	3.20	0.98897	8.00	6.42
0.99984	0.10	0.08	0.99403	4.10	3.28	0.98885	8.10	6.50
0.99968	0.20	0.16	0.99390	4.20	3.36	0.98873	8.20	6.58
0.99353	0.30	0.24	0.99376	4.30	3.44	0.98861	8.30	6.67
0.99937	0.40	0.32	0.99363	4.40	3.52	0.98849	8.40	6.75
0.99923	0.50	0.40	0.99349	4.50	3.60	0.98837	8.50	6.83
0.99907	0.60	0.48	0.99335	4.60	3.68	0.98825	8.60	6.91
0.99892	0.70	0.56	0.99322	4.70	3.76	0.98813	8.70	6.99
0.99877	0.80	0.64	0.99308	4.80	3.84	0.98801	8.80	7.07
0.99861	0.90	0.71	0.99295	4.90	3.92	0.98789	8.90	7.15
0.99849	1.00	0.79	0.99281	5.00	4.00	0.98777	9.00	7.23
0.99834	1.10	0.87	0.99268	5.10	4.08	0.98765	9.10	7.31
0.99819	1.20	0.95	0.99255	5.20	4.16	0.98754	9.20	7.39
0.99805	1.30	1.03	0.99241	5.30	4.24	0.98742	9.30	7.48
0.99790	1.40	1.11	0.99228	5.40	4.32	0.98730	9.40	7.56
0.99775	1.50	1.19	0.99215	5.50	4.40	0.98719	9.50	7.64
0.99760	1.60	1.27	0.99202	5.60	4.48	0.98707	9.60	7.72
0.99745	1.70	1.35	0.99189	5.70	4.56	0.98695	9.70	7.80
0.99731	1.80	1.43	0.99175	5.80	4.64	0.98683	9.80	7.88
0.99716	1.90	1.51	0.99162	5.90	4.72	0.98672	9.90	7.96
0.99701	2.00	1.59	0.99149	6.00	4.80	0.98660	10 00	8 04
0.99687	2.10	1.67	0.99136	6.10	4.88	0.98649	10.10	8.12
0.99672	2.20	1.75	0.99123	6.20	4.96	0.98637	10.20	8.20
0.99658	2.30	1.83	0.99111	6.30	5.05	0.98626	10.30	8.29
0.99643	2.40	1.91	0.99098	6.40	5.13	0.98614	10.40	8.37
0.99629	2.50	1.99	0.99085	6.50	5.21	0.98603	10.50	8.45
0.99615	2.60	2.07	0.99072	6.60	5.29	0.98592	10.60	8.53
0.99600	2.70	2.15	0.99059	6.70	5.37	0.98580	10.70	8.61
0.99586	2.80	2.23	0.99047	6.80	5.45	0.98569	10.80	8.70
0.99571	2.90	2.31	0.99034	6.90	5.53	0.98557	10.90	8.78
0.99557	3.00	2.39	0.99021	7.00	5.61	0.98546	11.00	8.86
0.99543	3.10	2 47	0.99009	7.10	5.69	0.98535	11.10	8.94
0.99529	3.20	2.55	0.98996	7.20	5.77	0.98524	11.20	9.02
0.99515	3.30	2.64	0.98984	7.30	5.86	0.98513	11.30	9.11
0.99501	3.40	2.72	0.98971	7.40	5.94	0.98502	11.40	9.19
0.99487	3.50	2.80	0.98959	7.50	6.02	0.98491	11.50	9.27
0.99473	3.60	2.88	0.98947	7.60	6.10	0.98479	11.60	9.35
0.99459	3.70	2.96	0.98934	7.70	6.18	0.98468	11.70	9.43
0.99445	3.80	3.04	0.98922	7.80	6.26	0.98457	11.80	9.51
0.99431	3.90	3.12	0.98909	7.90	6.34	0.98446	11.90	9.59

[*] Table abridged and reprint with permission from *CRC Handbook of Chemistry and Physics, 33rd Edition.* 1951–52, Copyright CRC Press, Inc. Boca Raton, FL.

Specific Gravity of Mixtures of Ethyl Alcohol and Water by Volume and by Weight
(continued)

Specific Gravity	% Alcohol by Volume	% Alcohol by Weight	Specific Gravity	% Alcohol by Volume	% Alcohol by Weight	Specific Gravity	% Alcohol by Volume	% Alcohol by Weight
0.98435	12.00	9.67	0.97608	20.00	16.26	0.95185	40.00	33.35
0.98424	12.10	9.75	0.97558	20.50	16.67	0.95107	40.50	33.79
0.98413	12.20	9.83	0.97507	21.00	17.09	0.95028	41.00	34.24
0.98402	12.30	9.92	0.97457	21.50	17.51	0.94948	41.50	34.68
0.98391	12.40	10.00	0.97406	22.00	17.92	0.94868	42.00	35.13
0.98381	12.50	10.08	0.97457	22.50	18.34	0.94786	42.50	35.58
0.98370	12.60	10.16	0.97304	23.00	18.76	0.94701	43.00	36.03
0.98359	12.70	10.24	0.97253	23.50	19.17	0.94620	43.50	36.48
0.98348	12.80	10.33	0.97201	24.00	19.59	0.94536	44.00	36.93
0.98337	12.90	10.41	0.97149	24.50	20.01	0.94450	44.50	37.39
0.98326	13.00	10.49	0.97097	25.00	20.43	0.94364	45.00	37.84
0.98315	13.10	10.57	0.97044	25.50	20.85	0.94276	45.50	38.30
0.98305	13.20	10.65	0.96991	26.00	21.27	0.94188	46.00	38.75
0.98294	13.30	10.74	0.96937	26.50	21.69	0.94098	46.50	39.21
0.98283	13.40	10.82	0.96883	27.00	22.11	0.94008	47.00	39.67
0.98273	13.50	10.90	0.96828	27.50	22.54	0.93916	47.50	40.13
0.98262	13.60	10.98	0.96772	28.00	22.96	0.93824	48.00	40.60
0.98251	13.70	1.106	0.96715	28.50	23.38	0.93730	48.50	41.06
0.98240	13.80	11.15	0.96658	29.00	23.81	0.93636	49.00	41.52
0.98230	13.90	11.23	0.96600	29.50	24.23	0.93540	49.50	41.99
0.98219	14.00	11.31	0.96541	30.00	24.66	0.9344	50.00	——
0.98209	14.10	11 39	0.96481	30.50	25.08	0.9244	55.00	——
0.98198	14.20	11.47	0.96421	31.00	25.51	0.9136	60.00	——
0.98188	14.30	11.56	0.96360	31.50	25.94	0.9021	65.00	——
0 98177	14.40	11.64	0.96298	32.00	26.37	0.8900	70.00	——
0.98167	14.50	11.72	0.96235	32.50	26.80	0.8773	75.00	——
0.98156	14.60	11.80	0.96172	33.00	27.23	0.8639	80.00	——
0.98146	14.70	11.88	0.96108	33.50	27.66	0.8496	85.00	——
0.98135	14.80	11.97	0.96043	34.00	28.09	0.8339	90.00	——
0.98125	14.90	12.05	0.95977	34.50	28.52	0.8161	95.00	——
0.98114	15.00	12.13	0.95910	35.00	28.96	0.7939	100.00	——
0.98063	15.50	12.54	0.95842	35.50	29.38			
0.98011	16.00	12.95	0.95773	36.00	29.83			
0.97960	16.50	13.37	0.95703	36.50	30.26			
0.97909	17.00	13.78	0.95632	37.00	30.70			
0.97859	17.50	14.19	0.95560	37.50	31.14			
0.97808	18.00	14.60	0.95487	38.00	31.58			
0.97758	18.50	15.02	0.95413	38.50	32.03			
0.97708	19.00	15.43	0.95338	39.00	32.46			
0.97658	19.50	15.84	0.95262	39.50	32.90			

Report Sheet—Experiment 9
Alcohol Content

Date _____   **Section number** _____   **Name** _____

1. Nature of sample: Product Name _____

   Brand _____

   Where Purchased _____

   Color _____

   Smell _____

   Taste if food product (optional) _____

2. Distillation

   (a) Observations during distillation_____

   _____

   (b) Distillate characteristics_____

   Color _____

   Smell _____

   Taste if food product (optional) _____

   (c) Temperature when distillate volume equals:

   1 mL _____ ° C

   10 mL _____ ° C

   20 mL _____ ° C

   30 mL _____ ° C

   40 mL _____ ° C

   50 mL _____ ° C

3. Density of distillate

    (a) Method used to determine density of liquid (hydrometer or Westphal balance)

    (b) Measured density of liquid   _____g/cm³

4. Percentage alcohol

    (a) % alcohol in distillate = % alcohol in sample

                                                      _____%
                          (specify % by weight or % by volume)

    (b) % alcohol in sample from label   _____%
                          (specify % by weight or % by volume)

5. Comments and conclusions on the experiment

Questions—Experiment 9
Alcohol Content

Date _____   **Section number** _____   **Name** _____

1. What do your temperature readings suggest about the effectiveness of your skill in separating out pure alcohol? Explain. What results would you have seen if all the pure alcohol had distilled off by itself?

2. How effective was the distillation in removing colored materials from your sample? What does this suggest about the volatility of these materials?

3. Now that you have performed this experiment, explain why it would have been impractical to distill all of the liquid from your 50 mL sample over into your receiver. In other words, why was it necessary to add the 25 mL of water to your flask before commencing the distillation?

4. The moonshiner makes white lightning in a big vat, which is later subjected to a distillation. What exactly does this distillation accomplish? Why is the "distilled product" better than the "vat product", or is it? Be specific.

Think, Speculate, Reflect and Ponder

5. How does the process of distillation relate to the fact that rain is usually substantially lower in dissolved chemicals than the surface water it falls into?

6. With the help of your lecture text or other source, list two important advantages of using "gasohol" motor fuels (gasoline containing alcohol).

    a)

    b)

Experiment

10

Why Is Water Harder Than Iron?

Sample From Home

Bring 200 mL of a water sample from a tap, well, or other natural sources.

Objectives

The chemical differences between soaps and detergents will be demonstrated and their respective advantages and disadvantages emphasized. The technique of titration will be used to compare quantitatively the effectiveness of both a soap and a common detergent in soft and hard water. Quantitative information using a standard hard water will enable the specific hardness value for an unknown sample from home to be determined.

Background

You are no doubt ready to argue that certainly water is *not* harder than iron. Ah, but it is if one defines hardness based on the concentration of calcium and magnesium ions, for in that case most samples of water would by such a definition indeed be "harder" than pure iron because calcium and magnesium ions are commonly found in water supplies. Admittedly some tricky semantics have been thrown at you, and in truth it must be acknowledged that such special hardness applies only to samples of water and not iron. This type of hardness has thus more to do with the chemical, rather than physical, characteristics of water. All official water analyses include data for the water hardness, since it plays an important and unwelcome economic role by causing

- chemical interference in some industrial processes;

- scale formation inside home and industrial plumbing installations;

- excessive consumption of soap.

These disadvantages of hard water are normally due primarily to the presence of calcium and magnesium ions, although the official analysis procedure determines the total amount of all group II alkaline earth metal ions in the Periodic Table. While calcium may be found in sewage and industrial effluents, the alkaline earth metals commonly found in water usually come from their soluble salts which have been leached out into ground water by water from surrounding rock strata. Limestone and dolomite are prevalent in the earth's crust and consist of calcium and magnesium carbonates. These minerals themselves are almost completely insoluble in water, but contact with acids which are present in all natural waters (most commonly due to dissolved carbon dioxide) convert these insoluble carbonates into the much more soluble bicarbonates. Calcium bicarbonate, for example, is 30 times more soluble than calcium carbonate, and is produced according to the reaction

$$CaCO_3 \quad + \quad CO_2 \quad + \quad H_2O \quad \longrightarrow \quad Ca(HCO_3)_2$$

calcium carbonate rock   carbon   water   calcium bicarbonate
(insoluble)   dioxide   (more soluble)

Magnesium carbonate behaves similarly to calcium bicarbonate. These bicarbonates are especially troublesome in boilers and hot water tanks, for heating water containing these salts produces an insoluble precipitate (scale). The heat essentially reverses the original reaction in which the bicarbonate was formed.

$$Ca(HCO_3)_2 \quad + \quad Heat \quad \longrightarrow \quad CaCO_3 \quad + \quad CO_2 \quad + \quad H_2O$$

calcium bicarbonate   calcium carbonate   carbon   water
(soluble)   (insoluble)   dioxide
                                         (scale)

Not only can these deposits result in seriously restricting and even stopping the flow of water as the scale builds up, but the scale layer seriously reduces the heating efficiency of the apparatus by acting as a heat transfer barrier. Because the heating and boiling of water containing such alkaline earth bicarbonates can remove the alkali metal ions by causing them to precipitate, the term *temporary* hardness is sometimes applied in such cases. If other kinds of alkali metal salts such as sulfates (e.g., $CaSO_4$, $MgSO_4$) are present, they are unaffected by heating and hence this kind of hardness is referred to as *permanent* hardness. Official analysis of water for total hardness (as well as the methods you will use in this experiment), however, measures all the calcium and magnesium (and other alkaline earth metals) salts present—bicarbonates, sulfates, etc.

Physiologically, hardness does not appear to be detrimental. In fact, hard water decreases the sensitivity of fish to toxic metals, and experiments with calves and chicks have indicated that those supplied with hard water develop somewhat better than those supplied with distilled water (containing none of these elements). And because of its mineral content, hard water is usually superior to soft water for irrigation.

Now that we have looked a little at the nature of hard water, we are in a better position to discuss the particular problem associated with hard water which is examined in this experiment—that of its effect on soaps and detergents and excessive soap consumption. All soaps, as well as detergents, have one basic feature in common—they consist of a long molecule, part of which is a nonpolar hydrocarbon chain which tends to dissolve in oil and grease (which are both nonpolar hydrocarbons themselves) and part of which is very polar or even ionic which tends to dissolve in water (a very polar liquid and good solvent for ionic substances). An axiom familiar to chemists is "like dissolves like". When a soap or detergent is shaken with oil and water, the long soap/detergent molecule binds together tiny oil and water droplets by virtue of the different solubilities of each end of its long molecule; each end dissolves in the substance in which it is most like.

dissolved
in water
droplet

dissolved
in oil
droplet

polar/ionic end of molecule   hydrocarbon end of molecule

Billions of these oil/water droplet combinations produce what is called an emulsion—a relatively stable mixture of oil and water. Once formed, this emulsion can be simply flushed away with water along with dirt particles, and the cleanser has thus done its job.

The large scale commercial preparation of soap today is basically the same as was practiced centuries ago with tallow and ashes—the splitting apart of animal or plant fats and oils with lye:

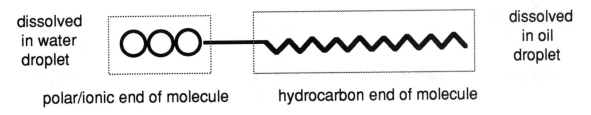

a fat   sodium   glycerol   sodium salts of 3 fatty
                   hydroxide   (glycerin)   acids ("soaps")
                   (lye)

As before, the boxed parts of the product molecules denote the oil soluble (right) and water soluble (left) ends of the molecule. Because of the nonuniformity typical of natural products like fats, R_1, R_2, and R_3 stand for hydrocarbon chains of differing length and structure. The best soaps are those in which the "R" groups contain between nine and seventeen carbon atoms. With fewer than nine carbon atoms, insufficient oil solubility and emulsification occur, while having over seventeen carbons makes the soap too insoluble in water to be effective.

Slight modifications in the chemical and physical makeup of soaps can give rise to a wide variety of familiar products: floating soaps (with air beaten in); soft or liquid soaps (using potassium instead of sodium salts of the fatty acids); castile soaps (using olive oil—a liquid fat—to make soap); transparent soaps (alcohol added to the soap mix); perfumed and germicidal soaps (appropriate chemical dissolved in soap). During the World War II people were asked to save their fats from cooking and take them to the local grocery from where the fats were sent to a central chemical processing plant. The desired product in this case was not mainly soap but the glycerin, a necessary ingredient for making nitroglycerin used in dynamite and smokeless powder formulations.

But what's so wrong with soaps that we need detergents, then? Acidic waters can precipitate some of the soap and thereby inactivate it. However a much greater problem lies in the fact that soap molecules will combine with certain metal ions such as the alkaline earths (and even certain heavy metals like iron ions) to give an insoluble precipitate.

$$2R-\overset{\overset{\displaystyle O}{\|}}{C}-O^{\ominus}\,Na^{\oplus} \;+\; Ca^{+2} \longrightarrow \left(R-\overset{\overset{\displaystyle O}{\|}}{C}-O^{\ominus}\right)_2 Ca^{+2} \;+\; 2Na^{+1}$$

| a soap (soluble) | calcium ions | calcium salt of soap (insoluble crud) | sodium ions |

The precipitated soap is what causes the familiar scum of "bathtub ring" and results not only in a clean-up mess, but also a significant waste of soap. Before any cleansing action can occur, enough soap has to be added to neutralize both water acidity as well as "neutralize" (precipitate out) all ions like calcium which are present in the water. Until the advent of detergents, the only alternatives to such scum and wasted soap were either to use rain water for washing, add other chemicals to try to tie up (inactivate) the acidity or calcium like ions, or install a Zeolite type ion exchange resin in the water supply system. When water flows over such a resin, the "hard" calcium/magnesium ions are exchanged for "soft" sodium ions, the resin thus acting as a water softener.

Then the 1950's marked the entrance of detergents. Like most all carbon containing materials we use, these compounds are derived ultimately from petroleum through chemical synthesis. The most common types of detergents are shown on the next page.

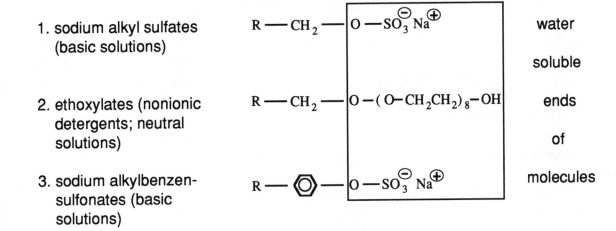

1. sodium alkyl sulfates (basic solutions)

2. ethoxylates (nonionic detergents; neutral solutions)

3. sodium alkylbenzen-sulfonates (basic solutions)

water soluble ends of molecules

Of these types, the sodium alkylbenzenesulfonates (ABS detergents) are the most widely used.

The big advantage common to all these detergents is the very one lacking in all soaps—the ability to clean in cold and hard water without being precipitated by acids or, especially, calcium/magnesium type ions. In fact, the calcium and barium salts of these compounds are used as detergent additives in engine oils. Furthermore, the cleaning action of detergents does not depend upon the formation of foam, which can be important in producing low-foaming cleansers necessary for automatic dish and clothes washers.

Prior to 1965, however, detergents suffered one very big disadvantage—they were not biode-gradable like soaps. Because of this, literally mountains of stable foam were not uncommon sights along waterways. Chemists discovered that this lack of biodegradability was due to the nature of the hydrocarbon chain "R". If this "R" group were made into an essentially straight carbon chain without any "side branches", bacteria could digest it and would indeed chew the detergent up thereby destroying it so it would not remain after use to pollute the environment. Today these microbially chewable detergents have replaced their earlier non-biodegradable counterparts. Studies have in addition shown that 10, 12, and 13 carbon atoms in the "R" group degrade the most readily, and are least toxic also to fish.

nonbiodegradable ABS detergent

biodegradable ABS detergent

Most commercial detergent products often also contain the following: water softeners (com-monly phosphates to tie up Ca, Mg, and similar ions); optical brighteners (special light absorbing chemicals which make clothes appear brighter); perfumes (for sales appeal); bleaches (to in-crease the whiteness of clothes, and enzymes (to remove protein-based soil and stains).

The official procedure for determining the total hardness of water calls for the titration of the alkaline earth metals with a reagent called disodium dihydrogen ethylenediamine tetraacetate (Na_2EDTA for short!) and uses a special color indicator to detect the end point. However, we can obtain reasonably accurate results by simply using a soap solution as the titration reagent, taking advantage of soap's normal disadvantage of being precipitated by alkaline earth ions. As soon as all the hardness ions have been thus precipitated, the soap will start to foam upon shaking, and that is our end point. Such a quantitative measure of the amount of soap solution required for foaming, together with a comparison to a standard hard water solution, will permit you to determine the hardness of an unknown water sample.

Whatever the hardness is due to, it is normally reported in units of milligrams of $CaCO_3$ per liter or, equivalently, parts of calcium carbonate per 1 million parts of water (ppm $CaCO_3$). You can quantitatively describe the extent of hardness of your unknown by reference to the following classification used by the U.S. Geological Survey and departments of public health.

Hardness (ppm CaCO₃)	Classification
0-60	Soft
61-120	Moderately Hard
121-180	Hard
Over 180	Very Hard

Procedure

Set up two burettes for a titration at your bench station using a double burette clamp. Refer to Experiment 13, *Vitamin C in Your Diet* regarding the preparation of a burette and the description of this procedure. You will also need four 250 mL Erlenmeyer flasks with stoppers all of which have been thoroughly cleaned with soap and hot water and rinsed with distilled water. Fill one burette with 0.5% detergent solution and the other with 0.5% soap solution to a level about 1 inch above the 0.00 line. Label the burettes so you will not mix them up later.

Open the stopcock and allow the liquid to fill the burette tip and wash out any air bubbles. When the meniscus level (recall Experiment 2, *Going Metric With the Rest of the World*) drops even with the 0.00 mL mark, shut off the stopcock and discard the reagent that has drained out. Examine the graduations on your burette carefully—both their numerical equivalent and the direction the numbers are increasing—to be sure you will read the meniscus levels correctly during the rest of the experiment. Ask your lab instructor if you have any questions or doubts on this before proceeding.

1. Detergent Titrations

Pour 50 mL of distilled water into each of two of your clean 250 mL Erlenmeyer flasks (you will not need all four flasks until **Parts 2b** and **c**) and proceed to titrate each of your duplicate water samples with the detergent solution. Since your "endpoint" in this titration will be the minimum amount of detergent solution causing the formation of a stable foam covering about 1/4 of the liquid surface which persists for at least 20–30 seconds, you will have to stopper your flask and briefly shake vigorously after addition of each 0.1 mL (2 drops) of detergent solution. Your lab instructor will demonstrate what such an "endpoint" looks like.

(a) Record data for the volume of detergent solution necessary to titrate the 50 mL of distilled ("soft") water to the nearest 0.1 mL. Repeat with the second 50 mL sample of distilled water. The two volumes needed to reach the end point for these duplicate samples should agree within 0.1 mL of each other. If not, run a third trial on another 50 mL sample of distilled water.

(b) Rinse out your flasks thoroughly with tap water, rinse with distilled water, and fill each with 50 mL of the standard hard water solution. Repeat the titration procedure as in **l(a)**, and record the volume data for detergent solution required to titrate each of your duplicate 50 mL standard hard water samples. As before, if the two detergent volumes do not agree within 0.1 mL, run a third sample. All of your detergent solution volumes required for each titration in both **Parts l(a)** and **l(b)** should measure under 0.5 mL.

2. Soap Titrations

(a) Pour 50 mL of distilled water into each of two of your cleaned 250 mL Erlenmeyer flasks and titrate as in **Part 1(a)**, only this time shake after each 0.25 mL portion (about 5 drops) of soap solution is added. Less than 1 mL of soap solution should be required, and your duplicate titrations should agree within 0.25 mL of each other. If not, run a third trial. Record all data on the report sheet.

SAVE your best titrated sample from **2(a)**—the one whose foam layer you deem represents the best end point—for the following titrations in **Parts 2(b)** and **(c)**. This soap/distilled water solution represents your *reference foam condition*, to which you can compare your foams obtained in subsequent titrations in order to be able to obtain good quantitative information.

(b) Pour 50 mL of the standard hard water solution into each of your three remaining cleaned 250 Erlenmeyer flasks and titrate as in **2(a)**. You will find it fastest to rapidly titrate the first sample shaking only after each 1 mL portion of soap solution is added. Your rough results from this titration should tell you the approximate volume of soap solution required to the nearest 1 mL. Now proceed to titrate the other two samples by adding the soap solution rapidly at first until you get to within 1 mL of the estimated end point. Then slow down and add the soap in 0.25 mL increments, pausing after each addition to shake and compare the foam produced in the sample you are presently titrating to that in your freshly shaken reference foam flask from **2(a)**. When the two foam layers match up, that is your end point. As in **2(a)**, duplicate titrations should agree within 0.25 mL. If not, run a third trial. Record all data on the report sheet.

(c) Rinse well, lastly with distilled water, the three 250 mL Erlenmeyer flasks used with the standard hard water samples from **2(b)** (but don't throw out your reference foam solution). Fill each flask with 50 mL of your own unknown water sample. Repeat exactly the procedure described in **2(b)** and record all your data.

The calculations which follow have you compute the "titer" of the soap solution—much like the titer described for the indophenol solution in the vitamin C experiment. The titer is simply a conversion factor which relates, in this case, a specific volume of soap solution with a specific equivalent amount of water hardness. This titer will permit you to convert from units of *mL of soap* into *ppm $CaCO_3$ hardness* for your unknown, just like you carry out a conversion from inches into centimeters. Necessary set-ups appear on the report sheet.

Report Sheet—Experiment 10
Water Hardness

Date _____   **Section number** _____   **Name** _____

A. Data

Trial

1. Detergent Titrations	I	II	III (Optional)

    a) Distilled (soft) water final burette reading _____ _____ _____

    Initial buret reading _____ _____ _____

    Net vol. detergent solution. (to nearest 0.1 mL) _____ _____ _____

    Average of two closest trials _____mL detergent per 50 mL of distilled water.

    b) Standard hard water final burette reading _____ _____ _____

    Initial burette reading _____ _____ _____

    Net vol. detergent solution (to nearest 0.1 mL) _____ _____ _____

    Average of two closest trials _____mL detergent per 50 mL of standard hard water water.

Trial

2. Soap Titrations	I	II	III (Optional)

    a) Distilled (soft) water final burette reading _____ _____ _____

    Initial burette reading _____ _____ _____

    Net volume soap solution (to nearest 0.25 mL) _____ _____ _____

    Average of two closest trials _____mL soap per 50 mL of distilled water.

	Trial		
	I	II	III (Optional)

b) Standard hard water final burette reading   _____   _____   _____

Initial burette reading   _____   _____   _____

Net volume soap solution (to nearest 0.25 mL)   _____   _____   _____

Average of two closest trials   _____mL soap per 50 mL of standard hard water.

c) Unknown hard water final buret reading
 (your sample from home)   _____   _____   _____

Initial burette reading   _____   _____   _____

Net vol. of soap solution (to nearest 0.25 mL)   _____   _____   _____

Average of two closest trials   _____ mL soap per 50 mL of unknown hard water.

B. Calculations

3. Titer of soap

(a) Volume of soap required to titrate standard hard water
(final line in 2(b))   _____mL.

(b) Volume of soap required just to make a foam
in distilled water (the "blank") (final line in 2(a))   _____mL.

(c) Net soap volume required to titrate just the hardness
in 50 mL of the 100 ppm standard hard water
(subtract line 3(b) from line 3(a)) =   _____mL.

(d) "Titer" of soap solution
(divide 100 ppm hardness by line 3 (c))   _____ppm hardness
per mL of soap solution.

4. Hardness of unknown water sample

    (a) Volume of soap required to titrate unknown water
    (final line in 2(c))   _____mL.

    (b) Volume of soap required just to make a foam in distilled water
    (the "blank" (line 3(b) above)   _____mL.

    (c) Net soap volume required to titrate just the hardness
    in 50 mL of the unknown water sample
    (subtract line 4(b) from 4(a))   _____mL.

    (d) Quantitative hardness of unknown water
    (multiply line 4(c) times line 3(d))   _____ppm hardness.

    (e) Classification of hardness (from table in lab background) _____.

5. Comparison on unknown

    (a) Geographical location where water sample taken   _____.

    (b) Water district from which unknown water sample taken   _____.

    (c) Official water district figure for total hardness
    (telephone to find out)   _____ppm hardness.

C. Comments and conclusions regarding experiment

Questions—Experiment 10
Water Hardness

Date _____   Section number _____   Name _____

1. Explain why the volumes of detergent solution required to titrate soft and hard water in 1(a) and 1(b) on the report sheet are so similar, whereas the corresponding volumes of soap solution in 2(a) and 2(b) are so different.

2. What is the source of the hard water ions found in water from ground water sources?

3. What former major environmental problem associated with the use of detergents has been largely overcome by chemical modification of the molecular structure of the detergent molecules?

4. List two advantages that detergents have over soaps.

(a)

(b)

Think, Speculate, Reflect, and Ponder

4. A problem of many cleaning agents is their phosphate content. Why are phosphates added, and what problems do they pose for the environment? (Consult your text for help, if necessary).

6. Did the Romans, quite successful plumbers in their own right, have problems with hard water? Why?

Experiment
11

The Staff of Life and Chlorine
A Representative Nonmetal

Samples From Home

Bring one slice of fresh bread or other food products suspected of containing salt. Crackers (6) or pretzels (3 large) may also be used. Bring them in a sealed plastic bag to prevent drying out prior to analysis.

Objectives

You will quantitatively determine the amount of moisture and salt in your bread or related food product and be introduced to techniques of ignition, precipitation, filtration, and drying. Some basic chemical reactions will also be illustrated.

Background

Chlorine can be found not only in things that feed us, but also in bleaches, insecticides, and poisonous warfare gases. It is indeed a versatile element which can either sustain or kill life, depending upon its chemical form and concentration.

You will utilize some simple chemical reactions to determine the amount of chlorine in a sample of your choosing. This chlorine will be present in the form of chloride ion—most probably due to sodium chloride (common table salt). After drying your sample to determine the amount of moisture present (moisture you—or someone—paid for), the product is ignited to burn away most of the organic compounds which would otherwise plug up the filter paper when the next step is attempted. The residue is extracted with water to dissolve out the salt, and a filtration is then performed to separate the salt solution from the insoluble charcoal residue. Since some of your salt containing filtrate remains with the residue and the filter paper, correction is made for this by a simple calculation shown at the end of the experiment.

When silver nitrate is added to the filtrate, the salt (NaCl) reacts according to the equation:

$$AgNO_3 \quad + \quad NaCl \quad \longrightarrow \quad NaNO_3 \quad + \quad AgCl$$

silver nitrate + sodium chloride   sodium nitrate   +   silver chloride
(soluble)   (soluble)   (soluble)   (insoluble precipitate)

The precipitate formed from treatment with silver nitrate is filtered from the solution, dried, and its weight determined. Note that its color changes during handling. Why? (HINT: Silver salts are basic ingredients in photographic emulsions.)

Although other ions besides chloride can also be precipitated by silver nitrate, the residue you see left on your filter paper is mostly silver chloride, AgCl. Since the amount of silver chloride will be small (perhaps 0.20 to 0.40 g), you will need to weigh your precipitate carefully if you expect to get meaningful results. And again, don't forget to zero your balance before you use it and use the same balance for all your weighings. Expect typical salt concentrations to fall in the range of 1–2% NaCl.

Procedure

1. NOTE: All glassware used in this experiment should be rinsed with distilled water before use.

    (a) Weigh one slice of bread (or about 20 g of some other food item thought to contain salt, such as 6 crackers or 3 large pretzels). Record this and all subsequent weights to the nearest 0.01 g.

(b) Dry your sample at 180 ° C for ten minutes (or until snappy crisp like Zwieback toast) and reweigh.

(c) and **(d)** Compute weight loss and percent moisture in your sample.

2. Break up your sample into small pieces and crunch into an evaporating dish. Place the dish onto a small iron ring mounted on a ring stand in a hood and heat strongly with a Meeker burner (or use two Bunsen burners) until burning and smoking ceases and the charred chunks remain in the dish (about 10 minutes). The dish bottom should have glowed a dull red during the latter part of this heating time.

(a) Record your observations from heating.

Clean a mortar and pestle with brush, soap, and distilled water. Grab the evaporating dish (it need not be cool) with tongs and use a scoopula to scrape out the charred chunks of residue into the mortar. Scrunch into granules with the pestle, add 50 mL distilled water, and stir for a couple of minutes.

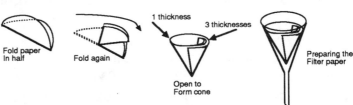

Place a long stemmed funnel into a ring mounted on a ring stand at your desk station. Fit it with a filter cone made from 12.5 cm paper (see Figure 11.1) and place a 50 mL graduate directly underneath (see Figure 11.2). Dump the liquid/solid contents of your mortar (called a slurry) all at once into a 400 mL beaker. Pour your liquid slurry in the beaker into your filter paper cone, taking care not to get the liquid level above the top edge of the paper cone. Collect 25-35 mL of clear filtrate, which should take 5-10 minutes. (The black solid left on filter paper may be discarded)

Figure 11.1. *Folding filter paper.*

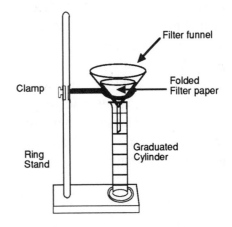

(b) Record the volume of the filtrate collected.

Figure 11.2. *Filtering water extract from bread residue.*

3. Pour your filtrate into a 125 mL Erlenmeyer flask, acidify with 5 mL of dilute nitric acid ($6M$ HNO_3) and add 15 mL of silver nitrate solution ($0.2M$ $AgNO_3$).

(a) What do you observe?

A white solid (precipitate) resulting from the step above indicates the probable presence of chloride ion. For confirmation and to obtain a quantitative determination (measurement of an amount), proceed as follows: Using a burette clamp, clamp the flask to a vertical rod so it rests directly on top of a wire gauze screen held by an iron ring. Heat flask contents to boiling with a Bunsen burner.

Continue boiling cautiously (watch out for excessive frothing) for one minute. Stop heating with the Bunsen burner and allow the precipitate to settle for a couple of minutes. If you have done things properly (and they must be for success here), the initially milky solution in the Erlenmeyer flask should now have a precipitate at the bottom with a mostly clear liquid (the "supernatant") on top. If your solution is still milky at this point, add a few more milliliters of 6M HNO_3 and boil for five minutes or until the precipitate coagulates and settles when the heating is stopped.

> **(b)** To check that all of the chloride ions have reacted to form a precipitate, add a few more drops of 0.2M $AgNO_3$ to the supernatant with a medicine dropper. No additional cloudiness should appear. If it does, add 10 mL of additional 0.2M $AgNO_3$ and repeat the boiling procedure.

4. Carefully (steady hand!) pour off (decant) most of the supernatant from the precipitate and discard it. Fit a filter funnel with a paper (Whatman #1, 9 cm or equivalent) and "slop" the small amount of slurry from your Erlenmeyer flask into the paper.

Wash the remaining bits of precipitate out of your flask and into the filter paper with two small (10-15 mL) portions of distilled water. Discard the filtrate. If squirt bottles of distilled water are available, hold the flask upside down over the filter paper cone and use a distilled water stream to wash out the remaining bits of precipitate.

When all the liquid has drained through, CAREFULLY—without tearing—lift the filter paper cone out of the funnel and gently place it upright nestled in the mouth of a 50 mL beaker. Set the beaker in an oven to dry 8 minutes at 180 ° C along with another empty filter paper circle of the same size. Remove the beaker from the oven using tongs or paper towelling and allow it to cool to room temperature.

> **(a)** Weigh and record to the nearest 0.01 g the weight of the filter paper and its precipitate.

> **(b)** Weigh and record the weight of the empty filter paper circle accurately to the nearest 0.01 g and record.

> **(c)** You should by now, if not earlier, be able to see some changes in the appearance of your precipitate since it was first formed in **3(a)**. Record your observations.

Like all calculations in this chemistry course, the computations called for here and in subsequent experiments can be solved using conversion factors. These conversion factors are given in the required set-ups for all calculations on the report sheets in this manual. No knowledge of algebra is necessary.

Report Sheet—Experiment 11
Chlorine: A Representative Element

Date _____   Section number _____   Name _____

1. Nature of sample (brand, etc.)_____

    (a) Weight of fresh sample   _____g.

    (b) Dried weight   _____g.

    (c) Weight of moisture in sample (subtract line 1(b) from line 1(a)) =   _____g.

    (d) Percent moisture in sample (divide line 1(c) by line 1(a) x 100) =   _____%.

2. "Bread roasting"

    (a) Observations_____.

    (b) Volume of filtrate   _____mL.

3. Precipitation

    (a) Observations upon adding silver nitrate_____.

    (b) Was any further cloudiness seen when a few drops more of $AgNO_3$ were added to the supernatant?

_____.

4. Filtration and collection

    (a) Dried weight of paper + silver chloride precipitate   _____g.

    (b) Dried weight of an empty filter paper   _____g paper.

    (c) Weight of AgCl in precipitate
    (subtract line 4(b) from line 4(a))   _____g AgCl.

    (d) What color changes do you observe in the precipitate?_____.

5. Calculations

(a) Calculate the amount of NaCl necessary to give your reported weight of AgCl:
(multiply line 4(d) by 0.41 g NaCl/g AgCl) = _____g NaCl.

(b) Total amount of NaCl in your original volume of 50 mL can be obtained from:
(divide 50 mL by line 2(b) then multiply by the grams in line 5(a) = _____g NaCl.

(c) Percent salt (NaCl) in original sample
(divide 5(b) by 1(a) x 100) = _____% NaCl.

6. Conclusion and comments regarding this experiment

If You're Not Part of the Solution

Then You're Part of the Precipitate

Questions—Experiment 11
Chlorine: A Representative Element

Date _____   Section number _____   Name _____

1. Explain the color change in the AgCl precipitate. (HINT: Think about the comment concerning emulsions used in photographic film.)

2. What is the difference between a chlorine atom and a chlorine ion?

3. From what naturally occurring mineral do we obtain practically all of our chlorine?

4. List two nonfood consumer products which contain chlorine (look for a chlor somewhere on the label).

Think, Speculate, Reflect and Ponder

5. Apart from salt and the need for it by most living organisms, what use does chlorine have which you regard as:

   (a) Most beneficial/essential for human beings and their environment?

   (b) Least beneficial/essential for human beings and their environment?

6. Why is the ocean salty and where does this salt come from?

7. Why is the large Cl symbol that is shown in the sketch* below pictured above a World War I battle field?

*Sketch reprinted with permission from *Contemporary Chemistry*, E. A. Walters and E. M. Wewerka, Merrill-MacMillan Publishers. Copyright Edward A. Walters.

Experiment
12

Meat Analysis:
Fat and Water
and
Protein/Carbohydrate Content

Samples From Home

Bring either 10 grams of ground meat (for instance hamburger or sausage) OR any other food containing significant amount of fat and water which has been finely diced/chopped before coming to lab (wieners, canned ham, bacon, etc.). Sample should be capped in a small jar or tightly wrapped in plastic to prevent water evaporation prior to analysis.

Objectives

The techniques of extraction and azeotropic distillation as defatting and drying methods will be illustrated through their application to the quantitative determination of the fat, water and protein/carbohydrate content of a student supplied food product. The results will be used to check both quantitative recovery techniques and, in the case of ground beef and sausage products, compliance of the food with legal regulations governing content. By analyzing different brands, a group of students can determine which brand of a particular product is the best buy based on protein/carbohydrate content.

Background

Since meat and meat products are normally sold by the pound (and maybe by the kilogram also someday soon), most consumers would like to avoid having to pay for excess fat or water—especially inasmuch as these ingredients cost just as much as protein! Sellers, on the other hand, would obviously like to sell as much water and fat as possible at protein prices. In the absence of any regulation, such protein prices for excessive fat and water is just what consumers would likely be gouged for.

The fat and water content of whole meat like steaks and chops are, of course, difficult to alter. Although water can be injected into some whole meat products like hams, altering must occur mainly through the diet and inactivity on the feed lot where most cattle are fattened up before slaughter. In the case of ground and processed meats like hamburger, wieners, sausage, sandwich cold cuts, and spreads, however, the sky is the potential limit when it comes to adding cheap bulking/extender agents, fat, and water. Fortunately, because of regulatory agencies, many of these food products must now adhere to legal limits and not "sky limits."

Federal standards require that any product labelled ground beef or hamburger contain not more than 30% total fat. No added water, binders, or extenders (like corn syrup, soybean meal, etc.) may be present. Since meats after grinding do not generally leave state boundaries, state and county agencies may also establish and monitor other "reasonable" standards. Some meat quality designations and fat limits appear in Table 12.1. Protein levels in these products will run about 1/4 of the water content.

Table 12.1. Some Whole Ground Beef Standards

Ground Beef & Chuck Designation	Maximum % Fat	Typical % Water	Regulatory Agency
Regular	30	55–60	Federal USDA
Lean	23	60–69	Some States and Counties
Extra–Lean	16	70	Some States and Counties
Leanest	9		Some States and Counties

(For a report on McDonalds McLean Deluxe Burger and similar competitive fast foods, see *Consumer Reports* July 1991.)

Federal regulations have been established for many other kinds of meat products as well. Whole ground sausage, for example, must contain only muscle meat and no organs. Some standards for sausage appear in Table 12.2.

Table 12.2. Some Whole Sausage Regulations

Whole Sausage	Maximum % Fat	Comments
Beef	50 %	Up to 3 % Added Water OK
Pork	50 %	Up to 3 % Added Water OK
Breakfast Sausage	50 %	Up to 3 % Added Water and 3 1/2 % Extenders OK

Pork sausage, for example, can be expected to contain typically at least 38% fat, which should be no surprise to anyone who has watched the sausage "shrink and swim" during cooking. Cooked pork sausages have been found to average 60% of original raw weight, although results varied widely (*Consumer Reports*, August 1968). For comparison, cooked weight of sliced bacon ranged from 30 to 40% (*Consumer Reports*, October, 1989).

Another widely sold type of meat product is cooked sausage like hotdogs and liverwurst (see Table 12.3). These come under United States Department of Agricultural (USDA) control as they normally *are* shipped across state lines. Cooked sausage products may contain no more than 30% fat and, since 1988, have also been subject to the 40% rule. This rule states that the percentage of fat plus the percentage of water added to the product by the processor must total no more than 40%. We can see from this formula that if the processors wish to make you pay for more "added" water (at "meat" prices), they will have to reduce the fat content accordingly. Federal regulations permit these cooked sausage products to contain up to 2 or 3 1/2% of certain non-meat additives like soybean meal and nonfat dry milk solids. Thus some of the protein listed on the label may come from these additives instead of from the meat itself.

Table 12.3. Some Cooked Sausage Regulation

Cooked Sausage Product	Maximum % Fat	Typical % Water
Franks, Wieners, Hotdogs, Vienna, Bologna, Liverwurst, and Thuringer	30 %	55–60 %
Salami, Cotto Salami, Pepperoni	30 %	Low

Actually, the various regulatory agencies have files of considerable analytical data for a wide variety of food products by brand name. But because these agencies treat the information as highly confidential, it verges on the impossible for the public to obtain access to these data, even though it was acquired through the use of public funds. It appears that a combination of a need to know, litigation, and application through the Freedom of Information Act may be necessary to make this information public. Even these long and very time-consuming processes do not guarantee success.

The background discussion of distillation in Experiment 9, *Alcohol Content of Beverages and Consumer Products* indicates that this superficially straightforward technique has indeed many not so simple ramifications. This experiment explores the practical aspects of the boiling together of two volatile liquids which, unlike those in the alcohol experiment, are not soluble (chemists say "immiscible") in each other. This process is known as azeotropic distillation. The word azeotropic refers to a constant boiling mixture, while the word distillation, of course, applies to a liquid boiling process.

Applied to your food sample, azeotropic distillation affords a neat method of separating the water in a way to permit rapid quantitative measurement of it, while at the same time also extracting out the fat and leaving behind a cooked, defatted, dehydrated residue of pure protein/carbohydrate. Tetrachloroethylene (a commercial cleaning and degreasing solvent) is a liquid which, when evaporated or boiled, will carry over with its vapors any water which is present. Because tetrachloroethylene is immiscible with water, the condensed vapors which drop out of the end of your condenser (the "distillate") will be cloudy as long as any water is present. As the liquid collects in your receiver, the dispersed microdroplets of water will come together to form a continuous water layer floating on top of the tetrachloroethylene.

And as an added plus, because tetrachloroethylene is a good fat solvent, the nonvolatile fat will dissolve out of the meat into the liquid tetrachloroethylene while in your distillation flask (the fat becomes "extracted" from the meat). When the distillation is stopped, all of the water will have distilled out, while all the fat will remain dissolved in the solution left in your flask. This solution can then be filtered and evaporated to yield the pure fat itself.

In keeping with the importance and theme of recycling our materials as much as possible on spaceship Earth, this experiment is designed so that most of the tetrachloroethylene used is recovered for use again by someone else. This organic solvent is nonflammable, but you should avoid breathing it or unnecessarily exposing its vapors to the air in the lab. Although it is less than 1/10 as toxic as the much more well known carbon tetrachloride, all chlorinated hydrocarbons can cause liver damage upon prolonged breathing and have also been implicated in the destruction of the ozone layer.

Procedure

(See the discussion of distillation in Experiment 9, *Alcohol Content of Beverages and Consumer Products.*)

1. Your sample must be ground, minced, diced, finely chopped or otherwise rendered into as small particles as possible. If you are analyzing a nonuniform product (e.g., a meat like bacon) try to take your sample so that it is as representative as possible of the entire large piece.

2. Set up a distillation apparatus as shown in Figure 12.1. Your whole apparatus should be clean, but must be especially bone dry. Acetone may be used (Caution: *Flammable*) to wash the water out of the inside of your glassware and speed drying (check with your lab instructor). Weigh out about ten grams of your sample on a square of waxed paper or plastic film to the nearest 0.01g and place into the 125 mL distillation flask. Insert a long stem funnel into the top of your distillation flask and add 50 mL of tetrachloroethylene (TCE) to the sample in the flask. The laboratory

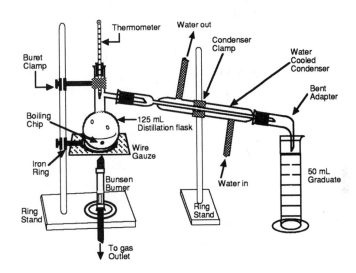

Figure 12.1. *Simple distillation apparatus.*

HOOD should be ON to exhaust any tetrachloroethylene vapors that might escape into the air. Use a spatula or solid glass rod if necessary to knock apart your sample if the pieces stick together in a lump. Reassemble your apparatus and have the lab instructor check your set–up before proceeding.

3. Turn on the condenser water until a gentle stream comes out of the exit tube. Bring the solution up to the boiling point quickly using a hot flame. When actual distillation of vapors over into your condenser begins, cut back the heat by partly closing the gas control valve to the Bunsen burner and distill slowly so that you collect an average of about one drop of distillate every two to three seconds (1 to 1 1/2 mL per minute). Another way to help control the heat and hence rate of distillation is to slide the wire gauze in and out so as to place open screen (more heat) or white ceramic center (less heat) between the burner flame and distillation flask. By sliding the gauze around you should be able to find just the right position to give you the desired one drop every 2-3 seconds distillation rate.

(a) What do you observe?

4. Continue distilling at this rate until 40 mL of liquid tetrachloroethylene (the bottom layer) has been collected in your graduate. This should take 30–45 minutes, by which time your distillate should have become almost, if not completely, clear, and you should have a distinct top layer of water in your graduate. If you are using a thermometer, the initial vapor temperature will hold around 87–95 ° C, creeping up towards 110 ° after 20–30 mL of distillate have been collected. Most of the water should be removed by then, but try to keep the temperature below 110 ° C as long as possible. By the time your final total lower layer volume of 40 mL is reached, the temperature should have reached at least 118 ° C or higher if all the water has distilled over as it should have (tetrachloroethylene itself boils 120-121 ° C).

Stop the distillation at this point.

It cannot be overemphasized that if you try to rush the distillation, you will not remove all the water and your distillate (liquid dropping out of condenser) will still be cloudy at the end of the distillation. The accuracy of your results would then suffer. Even in chemistry - especially so - haste makes waste.

> **(a)** While the distillation is underway, clean, dry and weigh an evaporating dish to the nearest 0.01 g so it will be ready for **Step 4(b)**. Note some identifying mark or number on the balance so you can use the same one when you reweigh this dish next period.

These next two steps are to be performed during the NEXT LAB PERIOD.

> **(b)** (Next Period) Weigh the evaporating dish containing the fat.

> **(c)** (Next Period) Note nature of fat residue.

After completing your distillation, carefully disassemble the apparatus so you can tip up the condenser and permit any water droplets "hung up" in it to run out into your graduate. SAVE the contents in your distillation flask for the Fat Content and Protein/Carbohydrate Content Determinations below.

If you have not already done so during the distillation, add a micropinch (about 1/4 the size of a BB) of a water soluble dye to the liquid in your graduate. This will dissolve only in the water layer and make it easier to see during the separation procedure which follows. If necessary, use a thin solid glass rod to reach down into the liquid and dislodge any obvious droplets of water which remain stuck to the sides of the graduate down in the tetrachloroethylene layer.

Using a long-nose medicine dropper, transfer all of the now colored top layer in your 50 mL graduate to a dry 10 mL graduate that has 0.2 mL graduations.

5. Read the total volume of your colored water to the nearest 0.1 mL and record. (Remember, read the bottom of the meniscus.) Discard the water layer and pour the 40 mL of TCE left in your graduate into the "waste TCE" container provided in the lab.

Examine the contents of your distillation flask. If you have measured all of your initial volumes correctly, you should now have about 10 mL of tetrachloroethylene containing the fat in your distillation flask, along with insoluble chunks of defatted, dehydrated, cooked protein/carbohydrate residue.

Gravity filter the distillation flask contents (solid pieces and liquid) by pouring them through a small filter paper cone (Whatman #1, 7 or 9 cm) mounted in your funnel held in an iron ring. (Refer to the experimental procedure in Experiment 11, *The Staff of Life and Chlorine* for the gravity filtration procedure). If you choose to "wet" the paper to make it stick better to the funnel wall, use tetrachloroethylene and not water. Have the filtrate drop directly into your previously weighed evaporating dish (**Step 4(a)** above). After the liquid has all run through, add about 3 mL of fresh tetrachloroethylene to the flask, swirl to rinse the sides and any residue, and pour into the filter paper cone in a manner that also washes the sides of the paper. SAVE all solid residue pieces for the Protein/Carbohydrate Content Determination.

Place the evaporating dish containing the 13 mL of fat solution onto a piece of paper with your name on it and place in the back of the hood until the next laboratory period. By then the tetrachloroethylene solvent will have evaporated leaving the pure fat ready to weigh and examine.

6. Transfer all the chunks of your insoluble protein/carbohydrate residue left from your filtration into a 50 mL beaker. Place this beaker in the hood alongside your evaporating dish to air dry until the next laboratory period.

These next two steps are to be performed during the NEXT LAB PERIOD.

    (a) (Next Period) Weigh your hard protein/carbohydrate chunks and report the yield.

    (b) (Next Period) Note the nature and appearance of your residue. You have prepared a cooked, defatted, and dehydrated food product. If your distillation flask was clean as directed, take a nibble of your goodies.

NOTE: The calculations called for on the report sheet will, in addition to assessing ingredient amounts (items number 7 and 8 in the calculations), also permit you to evaluate your own ability as a quantitative chemist (item number 10 in the calculations). Your total weight of water + fat + protein/carbohydrate would equal your ten grams of original sample if you achieved 100% recovery. Although it is possible to get good recoveries of fat and solids, expect about 10% of the water content to be lost during isolation (primarily through wetting of the condenser and upper part of the distillation flask). Thus your percent water in line 8a on the calculation page will represent only about 90% of original water in the meat sample. A closer estimate of the total water present can consequently be obtained by dividing your value on line 8a by 0.9.

Report Sheet—Experiment 12
Meat Analysis

Date _____   Section number _____   Name _____

Data

1. Sample Information

    (a) Kind of Sample_____.

      Brand_____.

      Grade (Regular, Lean, etc.)_____.

      Source of Sample (Where Purchased)_____.

    (b) Price of sample package or can_____.

    (c) Weight of sample package or can_____.

2. Weight of sample taken for analysis (to nearest 0.01 g)   _____g.

3. Comments on initial appearance of distillate

4. Fat Content Determination

    (a) Weight of empty evaporating dish (to nearest 0.01 g)   _____g.

    (b) Weight of evaporating dish and fat residue
    (to nearest 0.01 g)   _____g.

    (c) Nature, appearance, smell of fatty residue.

5. Accurately measured volume of water layer (to nearest 0.1 mL)   _____mL.

6. Protein/Carbohydrate Determination

    (a) Weight of protein/carbohydrate residue   _____g.

    (b) Nature, appearance and taste (optional) of solid residue

Calculations

7. (a) Weight of water
(Line 5 multiplied by the density of water, 1g/mL) =
H_2O.   _____g

(b) Weight of fat
(line 4(a) subtracted from line 4(b))   _____g.

(c) Weight of protein/carbohydrate (line 6(a))   _____g.

8. (a) Percentage of water in sample
line 7(a) is what % of line 2 (line 7(a) divided by line 2 x 100) =   _____%.

(b) Percentage of fat in sample
line 7(b) is what % of line 2 (line 7(b) divided by line 2 x 100) =   _____%.

(c) Percentage of protein/carbohydrate in sample
line 7(c) is what % of line 2 (line 7(c) divided by line 2 x 100) =   _____%.

(d) Are these values within legal/typical limits set by regulatory agencies? (See the tables in the introduction to this experiment.)

9. (a) Price per pound of purchased sample—Look on the package label or calculate:
line 1(b) divided by line 1(c) =   _____cents/pound.

(b) Price per pound of just the pure protein/carbohydrate in your sample
line 9(a) divided by line 8(c) x 100 =   _____cents/pound.

(c) How do your results in 9(b) compare with those for brands of similar products examined by other students, if any?

10. (a) Total quantitative recovery (lines 7a + 7b + 7c) =   _____g.

(b) Percent recovery
line 10(a) is what % of line 2 (line 10(a) divided by line 2 x 100) =   _____%.

(c) What do the results in 10(b) tell you about your quantitative technique?
(See the Note at the end of the procedure section.)

11. Comments and conclusions regarding experiment

Questions—Experiment 12
Meat Analysis

Date _____   Section number _____   Name _____

1. From your observations during this experiment, does tetrachloroethylene or water have the higher density? Why?

2. Describe what makes your distillate cloudy, and explain why this substance causes such cloudiness. (Hint: See the introduction to this experiment.)

3. What regulations for the food product you analyzed in this experiment that are not in effect now would you like to see enacted, if any?

Think, Speculate, Reflect, and Ponder

4. What foods are rich in protein besides meat products?

(a) Why are these non–meat protein foods a much more efficient protein source for man than meat in terms of the energy requirements and the land and water needed for growing?

(b) In spite of the efficiencies mentioned in part(a), consumers in the United States are still basically meat eaters. Why?

5. What will be the effect on the planet if all of the underdeveloped countries adopt the same meat production methods (energy, land, and water resource requirements) that the United States uses now?

Experiment
13

Vitamin C in Your Diet?

Sample From Home

Bring a liquid containing vitamin C. The color of that liquid should not interfere with the detection of the pink color formed in the reaction. Citrus juices such as orange and grapefruit—either fresh, frozen, canned, or powder—usually contain large amounts of vitamin C, whereas lime and lemon juices often contain small amounts. Expect apple, apricot, papaya, lime and white grape juices to have little vitamin C content (tomato type juices are an obvious no-no). About 250 mL (1/2 pint) of "drinking concentration" juice is desirable; half this volume would be the necessary minimum.

Objectives

An official governmental procedure will be used to determine quantitatively the vitamin C content of a sample from home. This procedure will illustrate the analytical technique of titration and color indicators. Calculations based upon titration results will permit a judgment to be made regarding the importance of the particular food sample examined as a source of vitamin C.

Background

If one were to heed the rhetoric of the drug and pharmaceutical industry, the only sure way to avoid malnutrition and disease is to become part of a completely 100% pill popping society. The "organic" drug manufacturers take things one step further by saying that the only good food, vitamin or drug is an organic one—not something made from foreign chemicals or dirty old gooey crude oil! We are now socked with advertisements even for "organic" cosmetics and hair shampoos, and whole "organic" vitamin display sections now can be found in many large stores, where rose-hip vitamin C and sea salt vie with their supposed "nonorganic" or "unnatural" counterparts for the consumer's dollar—and a lot more of it!

Vitamins are certainly important to individuals who suffer from malnutrition or specific bio-chemical disorders. These persons represent, however, only a tiny fraction of those who regularly take such dietary supplements. For the great masses it cannot be denied that vitamins can be effective as placebos—for instance a psychological uplift to the person who believes that they will help. In 1984, 1.4 billion dollars were spent on vitamin products in the United States. Vitamins and mineral supplements now constitute a $3 billion a year industry. Most of the persons making these purchases unfortunately were simply padding the financial pockets of the drug manufacturers for such psychological uplift. Furthermore, it has been shown that there can be too much of a good thing even with the vitamin panacea. Evidence has been published that points to the danger of ingesting too much of particular vitamins (specifically vitamins A and D) by the overuse of vitamin supplements.

As a type of compound, vitamins differ widely in their chemical structures. Physiologically, they may be defined as organic compounds that, while essential constituents of the diet, are required in only minute amounts. They thus differ from hormones in that the body cannot synthesize them, and they differ from trace elements because they are organic (carbon compounds). They also differ from fats, proteins and carbohydrates in that they are required in very small amounts. In an average daily diet of 600 g (on a dry basis), the total vitamin intake would represent only 0.1 to 0.2 grams. It is because the vitamins play an essentially catalytic role in life processes that they can be effective in such small doses.

Although claims for virility and sexual potency have not been touted (yet?) for vitamin C, this vitamin has received considerable attention in connection with general resistance to disease and particularly that elusive, incurable scourge—the common cold. No less a luminary than Dr. Linus Pauling, winner of two Nobel prizes (biochemistry and peace) has for many years now maintained that daily doses of several thousand milligrams of vitamin C can prevent the common cold (regular vitamin C supplements include normally only a few hundred milligrams or less). To date, the best evidence seems to indicate that vitamin C might indeed reduce the symptoms of colds, but not their incidence. But more hard evidence on this controversial question is still needed, for the long-range effects of the relatively massive doses called for by Dr. Pauling are not clear. Most excess vitamin C seems to be simply excreted unchanged in the urine. In the pure state, it is a colorless, crystalline solid.

Part of the problem is due to the practical difficulty of controlling and obtaining meaningful test results "in the field" (that is, out in the population). Compounding this difficulty is the fact that, although this chemical is important in promoting healing and fighting infection, the actual biochemical role of vitamin C (or L-ascorbic acid as it is chemically known) is still far from clear. Historically, we *do* know that the absence of adequate amounts of ascorbic acid in the diet results in the dietary disease called scurvy. The sailors who spent many months at sea on early ships much feared this disease until it was discovered that including fruit in the diet effectively prevented scurvy. The British Navy's solution to this was to include vitamin C rich limes in the food stores shipped on long voyages. The widespread eating of limes by the British Navy's seamen earned them the nickname "limeys."

Paprika (obtained from dried sweet peppers) has perhaps the highest concentration of vitamin C, although as a class of foods, the citrus fruits are probably most important. And because of their prevalence in the American diet, potatoes as well represent a significant source for this vitamin. Ascorbic acid is known chemically as a good reducing agent—which means that it undergoes oxidation very easily. This can happen slowly when ascorbic acid is exposed to oxygen in the air and is accelerated greatly by heating in air (most of the vitamin C content of foods is lost during cooking). This process can also be caused by other chemical oxidizing agents, and this special reactivity is made use of in this experiment: the particular oxidizing agent (indophenol) that we will use was chosen in part because the color changes accompanying the reaction are easy to observe.

The method used for your ascorbic acid determination is taken directly from the official procedure used by the U.S. Food and Drug Administration (FDA) and other regulatory agencies. During the reaction, the intense blue indophenol becomes decolorized as it is added to the ascorbic acid solution. So that you have the information to impress your friends and those around you, here is what the chemical picture looks like:

| oxidized form of indophenol sodium salt BLUE (in slightly basic solution) | oxidized form of 2,6-dichloro-indophenol free acid RED (in acidic solution) | L-ascorbic acid (vitamin C) | reduced form of 2,6-dichloro-indophenol COLORLESS | L-dehydro-ascorbic acid |

The box represents the reaction of indophenol with ascorbic acid. (The corner of each geometric polygon represents a carbon atom unless otherwise indicated.)

As the indophenol blue is added to the acidified juice sample, it would form a visible indophenol red color if it were not immediately oxidized to the indophenol colorless form by the ascorbic acid present. (As you might guess by looking at the equations, the color and light absorbing properties of molecules can be dramatically altered by subtle changes in their structure). At the exact point when the last bit of ascorbic acid has reacted, further addition of just a drop or two of the indophenol will produce a persisting red color due to the indophenol red form. In the controlled acidity of the juice solution, the indophenol turns red much like blue litmus paper turns red in acid. The indophenol is blue in your burette only because that solution is slightly basic (alkaline). Using an appropriate conversion factor (called the titer), this quantitative amount of indophenol used in the reaction can be converted into the amount of ascorbic acid (vitamin C) present in the sample.

It is desirable to use large volumes of juice in the experiment in order to reduce oxidation (and hence the destruction) of the ascorbic acid by the oxygen in the air prior to analysis. This method of analysis gives reliable results provided that the juice does not contain materials which (like ascorbic acid) also are reducing agents, such as oxidizable forms of iron, tin, copper, and SO_2 and sulfite or thiosulfite ions, all of which will interfere with an accurate determination.

Procedure

1. With frozen juices or drink powders, you should add enough water to dilute it up to "drinking strength" before proceeding. State the nature of your sample on the report sheet.

If your juice is not free of sediment, the pulpy juice should first be strained through several layers of cheesecloth held in place with a rubber band over the mouth of a 250 or 400 mL beaker.

Using a 50 mL graduated cylinder, measure 50 mL of your clear or strained juice into a 250 mL Erlenmeyer flask; add to it an equal volume of the metaphosphoric acid/acetic acid reagent and swirl to mix well.

Obtain a 25 or 50 mL burette and a double burette clamp and set up for a titration at your work bench. Your instructor will illustrate the techniques of this procedure. Basically, the burette is just a tall, thin graduated cylinder with a stopcock (valve) at the bottom which can measure out liquids (through this stopcock) to a high degree of accuracy (commonly to the nearest 0.01 mL). The process of quantitatively reacting or neutralizing another substance by metering out the exact required amount of liquid with a burette is called a titration.

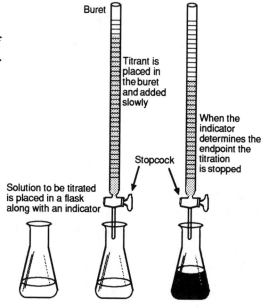

Figure 13.1. *Titration using a buret.*

Check your stopcock to see whether it turns freely. Ground glass stopcocks (but not those made of Teflon plastic) may require a LITTLE grease (too much will easily plug up the burette tip). See your lab instructor for help if necessary. If your burette is clean and dry, consider yourself lucky. If not, wash the burette with soap and water, rinse with a little distilled water and permit it to drain. A clean burette will not leave drops of water hanging to the sides. Lastly, rinse with a few milliliters of indophenol to remove any water left in your burette from the rinse.

Clamp the burette in its holder and fill it with indophenol reagent to about an inch above the 0.00 mL mark. Open the stopcock and allow the liquid to fill the burette tip and wash out any air bubbles. When the meniscus level (recall Experiment 2, *Going Metric with the Rest of the World*) drops down even with the 0.00 mL mark, shut off the stopcock and discard the reagent that has drained out (in the appropriate waste container). Examine the graduations on your burette carefully—both their numerical equivalent and the direction the numbers are increasing—to be sure you will read the meniscus levels correctly during the rest of the experiment. Ask your lab instructor if you have any questions or doubts on this before proceeding.

Using a 10 mL pipette with a pipetter bulb attached (a type like the "Propipetter" works well), transfer 10.0 mL of your juice/metaphosphoric acid/acetic acid mixture to a 50 mL Erlenmeyer flask. Place this flask onto a piece of white paper underneath your burette and proceed to "titrate" your juice/acid sample with the indophenol as rapidly as possible until a light but distinct rose-pink color persists for at least 5 seconds. The flask contents must also be continuously swirled to create proper mixing throughout the titration. The point at which a rose-pink color persists for at least 5 seconds is called the "endpoint" of your titration.

With most samples, the titration is begun by fully opening the burette stopcock. You will see that the solution in your flask immediately surrounding the stream of added indophenol turns pink for just a moment. With a little practice you will recognize how the slowness with which this pink color disappears can indicate how close you are to the final endpoint.

You will need to slow down as you approach the endpoint to a drop-by-drop addition. Remember: the flask contents must be continuously swirled to create proper mixing throughout the titration. Note the final burette reading and, after subtracting the initial reading, record the total volume of indophenol reagent added. You can expect 10–20 mL of indophenol reagent to be required per each 10 mL sample (called an "aliquot"). Record all volumes on the report sheet to the nearest 0.1 mL. (If you "overshoot" the endpoint, you will have to repeat the titration as described in the next step.)

2. Discard the titrated contents of the Erlenmeyer flask in the appropriate container and rinse the flask thoroughly with water. After doing this, repeat the previous procedure by titrating similar 10 mL aliquots of your juice/acid sample until you obtain two titration volumes which agree within 0.2 mL of each other. Record all your data on the report sheet. Note that in successive titrations the final burette reading from the previous run becomes the initial reading in the next run—this means that you don't have to fill up your burette to the 0.00 mL mark before each titration unless you will be exceeding the volume of reagent left in the burette during the next trial. You can now appreciate that the more highly colored your original solution is, the more difficult it will be to get a sharp color change at the "endpoint."

3. Your lab instructor will give you the conversion factor relating the volume of indophenol reagent and the milligrams of vitamin C present (the "titer" of the indophenol reagent); perform the calculations called for on the report sheet. From the results, state your conclusions as to the importance of a glass of your juice as a vitamin C source in one's diet.

> # Nothing Exists
> # Except Atoms
> # and Empty Space
> **Democritus 460–370 B.C.**

Report Sheet—Experiment 13
Vitamin C in Your Diet?

Date _____   Section number _____   Name _____

1. Nature of Product

   Appearance _____.

   Brand _____.

   Source of Sample _____.

2. Data: (Record all volumes to nearest 0.1 mL)

(a) Volumes of indophenol reagent required to titrate 10 mL samples of juice	Trial 1	Trial 2	Trial 3 (if needed)
(Final burette reading)	____	____	____
(Initial burette reading)	____	____	____
(Net volume indophenol used)	____	____	____

   (b) Average volume indophenol used _____mL.

   (c) "Blank" (Volume of indophenol necessary to give pink endpoint if no vitamin C were present)   <u>0.10</u> mL.

   (d) Net volume of indophenol required to titrate only the vitamin C present in sample (subtract line 2c from line 2b)=   _____mL.

3. Calculations:

   (a) "Titer" of indophenol reagent (mg of vitamin C equivalent to each 1.00 mL of the reagent) (get this from your lab instructor)   _____mg/mL.

   (b) Milligrams of vitamin C present in 5 mL of juice present in the 10 mL of juice/acid mixture (multiply line 2d by line 3a) =   _____mg vitamin C (per 5 mL of juice).

(c) Amount of vitamin C in a large glassful (Glassful = 10 oz = 300 mL)
(multiply 300 mL times line 3(b) and then divide by 5) = _____mg vitamin C
(per glassful).

(d) Glasses of juice required to obtain 100%
of the recommended daily adult allowance of 60 mg
(60 mg divided by line 3(c)) = _____glassfuls.

4. Comments and conclusions on experiment

Questions—Experiment 13
Vitamin C in Your Diet?

Date _____   Section number _____   Name _____

1. Precautions commonly found on bottles of ascorbic acid tablets say to keep the bottle tightly capped. Furthermore, the bottle itself is almost always dark brown or amber in color. Why?

2. One possible biochemical role sometimes suggested for ascorbic acid is its ability to prevent or at least diminish the oxidation of other critical substances crucial to normal body function, thereby acting to protect them from oxidative destruction. The ascorbic acid would thus be functioning as an "anti-oxidant." Explain the rationale for this. (Hint: If you were to sacrifice your life for someone else, that might be chemically analogous to the role of ascorbic acid in your body.)

3. In some areas persons used to be afflicted with a problem called goiter due to a lack of iodide ion in the food they eat. Nowadays this problem no longer exists.

   (a) Could lack of iodide in the diet be classified as a vitamin deficiency? Explain.

   (b) Why does this problem no longer exist?

Think, Speculate, Reflect, and Ponder

4. The danger of "overdosing" on vitamins seems to concern primarily just the oil/fat soluble vitamins. Which ones are they? And why is this so?

5. Taking large doses of vitamin C has been known to cause a decrease in the amount of B vitamins in the body. Knowing this, do you think B vitamins are more fat soluble or water soluble? Why?

Experiment
14

Label Reading—Know What You Buy, Use and Eat

Samples From Home

This is a nonlab experiment, but you will need to look at the following:

1. Products found in your kitchen, garage, medicine cabinet, grocery, discount, hardware, or garden store.

2. *The Merck Index* which can be found in the laboratory or in most libraries.

Objectives

The importance of reading labels on things we buy will be emphasized, as well as the usefulness of *The Merck Index* as a general source book for looking up the properties of label ingredients. The chemical and physiological properties of some selected drug, food additive, consumer product and "-cide" chemicals will be researched as a library assignment.

Background

A well known furniture polish contained a chemical which is classified as dangerous both to breathe and even to get on the skin. A widely advertised insecticide for continuous household use has as its active ingredient a close nerve gas relative. A very well-known headache formulation some years ago heralded their "new and improved" product to the public, not mentioning that the improvement resulted from the forced removal of one of the drug ingredients due to its implication in liver disease and cancer from prolonged use.

In all of these cases, the active ingredient in question was listed on the label. Admittedly, chances are that the chemical names will be mostly Greek to the average person. Most consumers will simply either not bother to read the label ingredients at all, or stop when reaching a word they don't understand (which may not take very long). After completing this assignment, the chemical names may still look like Greek to you, but at least you should know where to go to get some answers about their properties.

All this is not to say that we would, or should, do without many of the ingredients in things we buy and eat. Chemicals can indeed give us better things for better living, and most of us need not, nor would not, want to return to the oft, but ill-named, "good old days" of "natural" chemicals, foods, and products. Neither would most of want to live amidst "natural" 14-hour work days with "natural" 45-year life spans, natural health care, sickness, pestilence and early death!

Those individuals in the "natural" movement would do well to ask how much more "natural" their rosehip Vitamin C is than Vitamin C derived from glucose; how much better organic foods, cosmetics, or hair lotions are than the non-organic variety; how much better Bayer aspirin is than Brand X aspirin? Do these questions deal with fad or fact, truth or fiction? Do the properties of a chemical substance depend upon where its constituent atoms come from? How do "new" atoms differ from old or used atoms (recall the Recycling Aluminum Chemically experiment)? And what indeed is even meant by "natural" or "organic"? Are they just glittering catch words which advertisers hope will empty the pocketbooks of a gullible public?

Chemicals can, of course, be used to adulterate a product (grain, fat, water mixed into ground meat products), to conceal inferiority or damage in a product (food coloring of meats, fruits, and vegetables), and most alarmingly to promote an immediate "selling" effect to a product without sufficient or responsible evaluation of its possible toxic effects on the user (2,2-dichlorovinyl dimethyl phosphate in pest strips or nitrobenzene in furniture polish). Even when precautions are written on labels in print large enough to read, too many persons either ignore or seem contemptuous of these warnings.

For example, "Pest-Strip" (© Bio–Strip, Inc.; formerly marketed as Shell "No-Pest Strips") still contains the nerve gas relative 2,2-dichlorovinyl dimethyl phosphate (DICHLORVOS). Large boldface *red* type on the package announces that it is for continuous "use in homes, cabins, campers, garages, trailers, basements and apartments." In small *black* print follows the precaution: "Do not use in kitchens or . . any room where infants, sick, or aged are, or will be present, for any extended period of confinement." If you think these "red and black" statements sound almost like oxymora (contradictions in logic), you are not the only one. (See *Consumer Reports* May, 1988 and July, 1990.) Consumers Union has been warning against these products since 1967.

A more enlightened awareness and concern for chemical safety on the part of industries and the public are resulting in continued changes in the marketplace. Both of the potentially hazardous chemicals formerly present in the widely sold product "Scott's Liquid Gold" furniture polish have now been removed from the formulation. The nitrobenzene disappeared in 1983 and the trichloroethane in 1991. And what about that "New and Improved" product mentioned earlier? Anacin used to be just a high profile brand name for what were generically called APC tablets containing aspirin, phenacetin, and caffeine. In this case, less was better. Since becoming "New and Improved," Anacin has discontinued the use of the suspect ingredient phenacetin.

One also has good cause to wonder at the long-term health of those working in dry cleaning establishments. Do you feel like holding your breath when you are inside such a place? You should. But perhaps the most potentially hazardous chemical in your entire house (and indeed more dangerous than anything you can see around you, or will use, in the lab) can likely be found not in the garage or an outbuilding, but right in the kitchen—the aerosol can of oven cleaner containing potassium hydroxide. Read the label closely; if you think the warning sounds bad, just look up the properties of the active ingredient using the skills that you gain during this lab.

Procedure

Use *The Merck Index* handbook to complete the information called for on the report sheets, but do not expect to find information for all of the blanks for every compound. Most of this book consists of an alphabetical listing and description of chemicals according to their most common or chemically correct name. If you cannot find what you are looking for in the main listing, check the cross-index in the back of the book. Most substances have two or more possible names, and this cross-index lists many such synonyms by giving the locator numbers where you can find the description of the substance. The locator numbers are black and bold numbers assigned to each substance entry in *The Merck Index*. Copies of *The Merck Index* are in science laboratories and should be available also in most libraries. Some sample entries from *The Merck Index* are shown in Figure 14.1.

When making a list of ingredients to look up in *The Merck Index*, it is best to include some extras beyond the minimum of 12. There will probably be some chemicals that you will not be able to locate even in the cross-index. In such cases, don't become frustrated—simply choose another alternate ingredient from your list and proceed.

873. Aspirin. *2-(Acetyloxy)benzoic acid; salicylic acid acetate;* 2-acetoxybenzoic acid; acidum acetylsalicylicum; acetylsalicylic acid; Acetilum Acidulatum; Acenterine; Aceticyl; Acetophen; Acetosal; Acetosalic Acid; Acetosalin; Acetylin; Acetyl-SAL; Acimetten; Acylpyrin; A.S.A.; Asatard; Aspro; Asteric; Caprin; Claradin; Colfarit; Contrheuma retard; Cosprin; Delgesic; Duramax; ECM; Ecotrin; Empirin; Encaprin; Endydol; Entrophen; Enterosarine; Helicon; Levius; Longasa; Measurin; Neuronika; Platet; Rhodine; Salacetin; Salcetogen; Saletin; Solprin; Solpyron; Xaxa. $C_9H_8O_4$; mol wt 180.15. C 60.00%, H 4.48%, O 35.53%. Prepn: C. Gerhardt, *Ann.* **87,** 149 (1853). Manuf from salicylic acid and acetic anhydride: Faith, Keyes & Clark's *Industrial Chemicals,* F. A. Lowenheim, M. K. Moran, Eds. (Wiley-Interscience, New York, 4th ed., 1975) pp 117-120. Crystallization from acetone: Hamer, Phillips, **U.S.** pat. **2,890,240** (1959 to Monsanto). Novel process involving distillation: Edmunds, **U.S.** pat. **3,235,583** (1966 to Norwich Pharm.). Crystal structure: P. J. Wheatley, *J. Chem. Soc. (Suppl.)* **1964,** 6036. Toxicity data: E. R. Hart, *J. Pharmacol. Exp. Ther.* **89,** 205 (1947). Evaluation as a risk factor in Reye's syndrome: P. J. Waldman *et al., J. Am. Med. Assoc.* **247,** 3089 (1982). Review of clinical trials in prevention of myocardial infarction and stroke: P. C. Elwood, *Drugs* **28,** 1-5 (1984). Symposium on aspirin therapy: *Am. J. Med.* **74,** no. 6A, 1-109 (1983). Comprehensive description: K. Florey, Ed. in *Analytical Profiles of Drug Substances,* **vol. 8** (Academic Press, New York, 1979) pp 1-46. Monograph: M. J. H. Smith, P. K. Smith, *The Salicylates* (Interscience, New York, 1966) 313 pp. Book: *Acetylsalicylic Acid,* H. J. M. Barnett *et al.,* Eds. (Raven, New York, 1982) 278 pp.

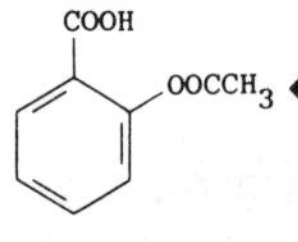

Monoclinic tablets or needle-like crystals. d 1.40. mp 135° (rapid heating); the melt solidifies at 118°. uv max (0.1*N* H_2SO_4): 229 nm ($E^{1\%}_{1cm}$ 484); ($CHCl_3$): 277 nm ($E^{1\%}_{1cm}$ 68). Is odorless, but in moist air it is gradually hydrolyzed into salicylic and acetic acids and acquires the odor of acetic acid. Stable in dry air. pK (25°) 3.49. One gram dissolves in 300 ml water at 25°, in 100 ml water at 37°, in 5 ml alcohol, 17 ml chloroform, 10-15 ml ether. Less soluble in anhydr ether. Decomp by boiling water or when dissolved in solns of alkali hydroxides and carbonates. LD_{50} orally in mice, rats (g/kg): 1.1, 1.5 (Hart).

THERAP CAT: Analgesic; antipyretic; anti-inflammatory.

THERAP CAT (VET): Analgesic; antipyretic; antirheumatic; anticoagulant.

CROSS INDEX OF NAMES

Asphaltum *see* 867
Asphocalcium *see* 855
Aspiculamycin *see* 4436
Aspidin, 868
Aspidinol, 869
Aspidium, 870
Aspidol [Piam] *see* 5510
Aspidosperma, 871
Aspidospermine, 872
Aspirin, 873
Aspirin Aluminum *see* 328
Aspirin Lysine Salt *see* 5510
Aspisol [Bayer] *see* 5510
Aspogen [Eaton] *see* 3168
Aspoxicillin, 874
Aspro [Nicholas] *see* 873
Assaren [Permamed] *see* 3071
Assert [Am. Cyanamid] *see* 4825
Assiprenol *see* 5105
Assugrin *see* 2707
Assur *see* 6181
Assure [Nissan] *see* 8113
Asta C 4898 *see* 3185
Astacene *see* 875
Astacin, 875
Astaril *see* 3807
Astatine, 876
Astaxanthin, 877
Asta Z 4942 *see* 4822
ATBAC *see* 1757
ATC [Medial] *see* 9375
Atcotibine *see* 5071
Ateben [Chem-Sintyal] *see* 6635
Atebrin Hydrochloride *see* 8053
Ateculon [Nippon Chemiphar] *see* 2374
AteHexal [Hexal] *see* 879
Atelor [Roche] *see* 2967
Atem [Chiesi] *see* 4960
Atemorin *see* 5731
Atempol [Norgine] *see* 5731
Atenen [Tsuruhara] *see* 145
Atenezol [Tsuruhara] *see* 45
Atenol [CT] *see* 879
Atenolol, 879
Atenos [UCB] *see* 9720
Atenos *see* 1799
Atensil *see* 7394
Atensin *see* 5737
Atensine [Berk] *see* 2977
Aterax *see* 4786
Aterian *see* 8879
Ateriosan *see* 2374
Ateroid [Mack, Illert.] *see* 2217
Aterosan [Lancet] *see* 7987
Atgard [Shell] *see* 3069
Athamantin, 880
Atheran *see* 2380

Figure 14.1. *Cross index and aspirin entry from The Merck Index*.*

Table 14.1 beginning on the page154 is a partial listing of the Food and Drug Administration's list of "Generally Recognized as Safe" food additives which you can use to catagorize your food additives.

*Reproduced from *The Merk Index*, Eleventh Edition (1989), S. Budavari, M. J. O'Neil, A. Smith, P. E. Heckelman, Eds., by permission of the copyright owner, Merck & Co., Inc., Rahway, NJ, U.S.A. © Merck & Co., 1989.

The categories of ingredients that you will need to research are:

A. "-Cides": (Insecticides, pesticides, fungicides, herbicides, algaecides, rodenticides). All these are "killer" chemicals. Locate two or more "cide" products representing four different active ingredients total.

B. Drugs: Locate two or more pharmaceutical/medicinal products representing four different active ingredients total.

C. Consumer Products: (Things that you use, in your home, kitchen, garage, or on yourself—such as cosmetics, cleaners, paint removers, polishes, etc.). The labels may prove somewhat skimpy on chemical details in this category, but you should be able to come up with two or more products representing four different ingredients total.

D. Food Additives: Locate various food products containing a total of four different additives found in at least three of the eight categories listed below:

Anticaking agents

Chemical preservatives

Emulsifying agents

Nutrients and dietary supplements

Sequestrants

Stabilizers

Synthetic flavoring substances

Multiple purpose and miscellaneous additives

To facilitate your search and get you started, one entry has already been provided in each category on the report sheets as a guide. This leaves only three more ingredients that you must look up in each category. The total of all the compounds will be sixteen—12 checked by you and 4 that have been provided.

Further information on food additives can be found in the following books:

1. *Food Additives* by Taylor

2. *Consumer's Dictionary of Food Additives* by Ruth Winter

3. *Food Additives Book* from Consumer's Union

Table 14.1. Direct Food Substances Generally Recognized as Safe Partial Listing of Additives in Food and Drug Administration's "GRAS" List*

Anticaking Agents

Aluminum calcium silicate
Calcium silicate
Magnesium silicate
Sodium aluminosilicate
Sodium calcium
    aluminosilicate
Tricalcium silicate

Chemical Preservatives

Ascorbic acid
Ascorbyl palmitate
Benzoic acid
Butylated hydroxyanisole
Butylated hydroxytoluene
Calcium ascorbate
Calcium propionate
Calcium sorbate
Dilauryl thiodipropionate
Erythorbic acid
Methylparaben
Potassium bisulfite
Potassium metabisulfite
Potassium sorbate
Propionic acid
Propyl gallate
Propylparaben
Sodium ascorbate
Sodium benzoate
Sodium bisulfite
Sodium metabisulfite
Sodium propionate
Sodium sorbate
Sodium sulfite
Sorbic acid
Stannous chloride
Sulfur dioxide
Thiodipropionic acid
Tocopherols

Emulsifying Agents

Diacetyl tartaric acid esters
    of mono- and diglycerides
Mono- and diglycerides of
    fats and oils
Monosodium phosphate derivatives
of the above
Propylene glycol
Ox bile extract

Nutrients and Dietary Supplements

Ascorbic acid
Biotin
Calclum carbonate
Calcium citrate
Calclum glycerophosphate
Calcium oxide
Calcium pantothenate
Calcium phosphate
Calcium pyrophosphate
Calcium sul fate
Carotene
Choline bitartrate
Choline chloride
Copper gluconate
Cuprous iodide
Cysteine
Ferric phosphate
Ferric pyrophosphate
Ferric sodium pyrophosphate
Ferrous gluconate
Ferrous lactate
Ferrous sulfate
Inositol
Iron, reduced
Linoleic acid
Magnesium oxide
Magnesium phosphate
Magnesium sulfate
Manganese chloride
Manganese citrate
Manganese gluconate
Manganese glycerophosphate
Manganese sulfate
Manganous oxide
Niacin
Niacinamide
D-pantothenyl alcohol
Potassium chloride
Potassium glycerophosphate
Potassium iodide
Pyridoxine hydrochloride
Riboflavin
Riboflavin-5-phosphate
Sodium pantothenate
Sodium phosphate
Sorbitol
Thiamine hydrochloride
Thiamine mononitrate
Tocopherols
Tocopherol acetate
Vitamin A
Vitamin A acetate

Vitamin A palmitate
Vitamin B_{12}
Vitamin D_2
Vitamin D_3
Zinc chloride
Zinc gluconate
Zinc oxide
Zinc stearate
Zinc sulfate

Sequestrants

Calcium acetate
Calcium chloride
Calcium citrate
Calcium diacetate
Calcium gluconate
Calcium hexametaphosphate
Calcium phosphate,
    monobasic
Citric acid
Dipotassium phosphate
Disodium phosphate
Isopropyl citrate
Monoisopropyl citrate
Potassium citrate
Sodium acid phosphate
Sodium citrate
Sodiuum diacetate
Sodium gluconate
Sodium hexametaphosphate
Sodium metaphosphate
Sodium phosphate
Sodium potassium tartrate
Sodium pyrophosphate
Sodium pyrophosphate,
    tetra
Sodium tartrate
Sodium thiosulfate
Sodium tripoly-
    phosphate
Stearyl citrate
Tartaric acid

Stabilizers

Acacia (gum arabic)
Agar-agar
Ammonium alginate
Calcium alginate
Carob bean gum
Chondrus extract
Ghatti gum
Guar gum

*Selected from Code of Federal Regulations, Foods & Drugs, Office of the Federal Register; 1985.

Table 14.1. (*continued*)

Potassium alginate
Sodium alginate
Sterculia (karaya) gum
Tragacanth

Synthetic Flavoring Substances

Acetaldehyde
Acetoin
Anethole
Benzaldehyde
N-butyric acid
d- or l-carvone
Cinnamaldehyde
Citral
Decanal
Diacetyl
Ethyl acetate
Ethyl butyrate
Ethyl vanillin
Eugenol
Geraniol
Geranyl acetate
Glycerol tributyrate
Limonene
Linalool
Linalyl acetate
Methyl anthranilate
3-Methyl-3-phenylglycidic
    acid ethyl ester
Piperonal
Vanillin

Multiple Purpose and Miscellaneous Additives

Acetic acid
Aconitic acid
Adipic acid
Alginic acid
Brown algae
Red algae
Aluminum ammonium
    sulfate
Aluminum potassiun sulfate
Aluminum sodium sulfate
Aluminum sulfate
Ammonium bicarhonate
Ammonium carbonate
Ammonium chloride
Ammonium hydroxide
Ammonium phosphate,
    monobasic

Ammonium phosphate,
    dibasic
Ammonium sulfate
Bakers yeast extract
Beeswax (yellow and white)
Bentonite
n-Butane and isobutane
Caffeine
Calcium hydroxide
Calcium iodate
Calcium lactate
Calcium stearate
Candelilla wax
Caprylic acid
Caramel
Carbon dioxide
Carnauba wax
Mixed carbohydrase and
        protease enzyme product
Carngluten
Clove and its derivatives
Cocoa butter substitute
    primarily from palm oil
Copper sulfate
Corn silk and corn silk extract
L-Cysteine monohydrochloride
Dextrin
Dextrans
Diacetyl
Dill and its derivatives
Ethyl alcohol
Ethyl formate
High fructose corn syrup
Garlic and its derivatives
Insoluble glucose isomerase
        enzyme preparations
Glutamic acid
Glutamic acid hydrochloride
Glycerin
Glyceryl monostearate
Helium
Hydrochloric acid
Hydrogen peroxide
Lactase enzyme preparation
        from *kluyveromyces lactis*
Lactic acid
Lecithin
Ground limestone
Maltodextrin
Malt syrup (malt extract)
Methylparaben
Magnesium carbonate
Magnesium hydroxide
Magnesium stearate
Malic acid

Methylcellulose
Monoammonium glutamate
Monopotassium glutamate
Nickel
Nitrogen
Nitrous oxide
Ozone
Panain
Pectins
Peptones
Phosphoric acid
Potassium acid tartrate
Potassium bicarbonate
Potassium carbonate
Potassium hydroxide
Potassium sulfate
Potassium iodate
Propane
Pyridoxine hydrochloride
Rennet (animal derived)
Rapeseed oil
Rue
Oil of rue
Silica aerogel
Sodium acetate
Sodium aluminum phosphate
Sodium bicarbonate
Sodium carbonate
Sodium carboxymethyl-
cellulose
Sodium caseinate
Sodium hypophosphite
Sodium hydroxide
Sodium pectinate
Sodium phosphate
Sodium sesquicarbonate
Stearic acid
Succinic acid
Sulfuric acid
Tartaric acid
Triacetin
Triethyl citrate
Urea
Wheat gluten
Whey
Reduced lactose whey
Reduced minerals whey
Whey protein concentrate
Zein

Report Sheet—Experiment 14
Label Reading—Know What You Buy, Use and Eat

Date _____   Section number _____   Name _____

(A) "-Cides"	Brand and Product Name	Ingredient Name	Alternate Chemical Name	Formula	Uses	Side Affects Contra-indications	Toxicity LD$_{50}$
(1) Rodenticide	Havoc	Brodifacoum	Talon	$C_{31}H_{23}BrO_3$	Kills mice and rats	——	0.27 mg/kg in rats
(2)							
(3)							
(4)							

Date _____   Section number _____   Name _____

(B) Drugs	Brand and Product Name	Ingredient Name	Alternate Chemical Name	Formula	Uses	Side Affects Contra-indications	Toxicity LD_{50}
(1) Sheep and Horse wormer	Eqvalan paste	Ivermectin	22, 23-dihydro-avermectin	$C_{48}H_{74}O_{14}$	Anti—parasitic	Do not use in dogs	———
(2)							
(3)							
(4)							

Date _____   Section number _____   Name _____

(C) Consumer Products	Brand and Product Name	Ingredient Name	Alternate Chemical Name	Formula	Uses	Side Affects Contra-indications	Toxicity LD$_{50}$
(1) Paint Remover	Zip-Strip	Methylene Chloride	Dichloro Methane	CH_2Cl_2	Solvent, Degreasing Fluid	Narcotic	—
(2)							
(3)							
(4)							

Report Sheet—Experiment 14
Label Reading—Know What You Buy, Use and Eat

Date _____   Section number _____   Name _____

(D) Food Additives	Brand and Product Name	Ingredient Name	Alternate Chemical Name	Formula	Uses	Side Affects Contra-indications	Toxicity LD_{50}
(1) Anti-caking Agent	Leslie Iodized salt	Aluminum Calcium Silicate	Calcium Aluminosilicate	$CaAl_2Si_2O_8$ and $Ca_2Al_2SiO_7$	Also used in cement	—	—
(2)							
(3)							
(4)							

Experiment

15

Chromatography of Artificial Colors

Samples From Home

No samples from home are need for this experiment.

Objectives

This experiment introduces you to the world of artificial colors by allowing you to separate a solution that appears to be a single component into the separate dyes that act together to give the mixture its color. The technique of separation used in this experiment is called liquid chromatography.

Background

Hundreds of thousands of pounds of artificial colors are added to food, drugs and cosmetics each year in the United States. This artificial coloring is used solely to enhance the visual appeal of the product to the consumer. Artificial colors are regulated in the United States by the Food and

Drug Administration (FDA) under the Food, Drug and Cosmetics Act. Regulation in this area was first instituted in 1906 when seven dyes were allowed. One of these, "Butter Yellow", was banned in 1932 when research showed that it caused liver tumors in rats. By 1950, the list of approved dyes had expanded to nineteen. In that year, three of the approved dyes were removed from the list when children eating popcorn colored with them became sick. More recently, FD&C (Food, Drug, and Cosmetic) Red 2 was banned by the Food and Drug Administration in 1976, again based upon cancer concerns. Presently there are seven dyes approved for use in food in the United States and a few more approved for dying things like orange skins (Citrus Red 2) that are not supposed to be consumed.

Many consumer products have more than one added artificial dye. Many popular "fruit" drinks, for instance, a staple in American childhood, often have two and sometimes three or more dyes added to yield those pleasing bright colors that make them so attractive to children. In this experiment you will separate a few of the dyes that have been added to some consumer products using a small plastic cartridge called a Sep Pak® and a separation technique called liquid chromatography.

The purpose of all chromatography is to separate mixtures into individual components. Liquid chromatography gets its name from the procedure of passing a **liquid** mixture through a porous solid (called the stationary phase) that has been packed into a (usually) metal column. This mixture is dissolved in a solvent, called the mobile phase, that is pumped continually through the chromatographic column. As the liquid components in the mixture pass through the column, they are attracted by differing amounts to the stationary phase packed in the column. Actually, they go through repeated cycles of "dissolving" in the stationary phase then redissolving into the moving mobile phase and moving down the column again before interacting with the solid phase again. This cycle occurs over and over again. Since the way or amount that each component in the mixture does this is slightly different (that is more or less interaction) the components become separated from each other by the time they reach the column's end. The end of the column is where the separated components are detected or in our case collected for further analysis.

Procedure

Caution: *Methanol is poisonous and flammable. Use care when handling this solvent.*

1. Line up 10 test tubes (150 mm; 6 inch) against a white background in your test tube rack. Fill a 100 mL beaker with water and another with methanol. Mark these beakers with labels or a grease pencil.

2. Draw 10 mL of methanol into a 25 mL syringe. This, therefore, is 10 mL of 100% methanol. Attach the syringe to the **short end** of the Sep Pak cartridge. Almost any 25 mL or larger disposable syringe with removable needles will fit. Flush the Sep Pak cartridge with the methanol by pressing the plunger slowly all the way to the bottom. Direct the methanol that is exiting (eluting) from the cartridge into an appropriate waste beaker. Press the syringe plunger down in such a way that approximately 3 drops per second come out of the end of the cartridge. You cannot depress the plunger too slowly; however, if you press too hard liquid will leak out of the connection between the syringe and the cartridge or it will squirt out from behind the plunger back up the barrel of the syringe.

3. Repeat the flushing process by drawing 5 mL of water into the syringe with the cartridge disconnected and then passing the water through the reconnected cartridge. Disconnect the cartridge from the syringe and get 50 mL of an unknown dye mixture from the lab instructor. **Record your unknown number and its initial color on the report sheet.**

4. Draw 5 mL of your unknown dye mixture into the syringe. Reconnect the syringe to the short end of the cartridge, and slowly pass the mixture through the cartridge into the waste beaker. The liquid eluting (exiting) from the cartridge will be relatively clear, while the dyes in the unknown mixture will stay on the cartridge. This is called charging the column.

5. Experimentally we now need to design a scheme using different mixtures of methanol and H_2O that will allow you to determine correctly the total number of different color dyes in your unknown mixture. Total volumes of 10 mL are probably best for any mixture of solvents that you choose. Keep a listing of the mixtures that you use in case you need to repeat or refine your procedure. For example, if you want to start with a 100% water "mixture", then draw 10 mL of water in the syringe, connect the charged cartridge and slowly pass the solvent through the cartridge, collecting the liquid in a test tube that is eluting from the cartridge. Next try a 90% water/10% methanol mixture. This can be made by drawing 9 mL of water into the syringe and then without expelling the water drawing 1 mL of methanol into the syringe. This solution can then be successfully mixed by drawing a 3 mL air bubble into the syringe and inverting the syringe repeatedly. Make sure that you get rid of the air bubble before you start to pass the solvent onto the cartridge. As you elute these water/methanol mixtures (that is, pass them one by one through the syringe and cartridge), individual colored dyes will start to come off of your chromatographic column (the cartridge). Collect these in test tubes as they exit from the cartridge. You may be able to see the colored bands as they separate and move down the cartridge since the wall of the Sep Pak is a relatively thin, white plastic.

6. As you see a change in the color of the solvent eluting from the syringe, collect it in another test tube. If it becomes obvious that you have mixed two colors and you want to begin again, pass 20 mL of methanol and then 5 mL of water through the cartridge (into the waste beaker) and start again at **Step 4**.

7. Repeat this process until you have as many test tubes as possible with different colors in them. Try your best to make each test tube as monochromatic (containing only one color) as possible. For instance, a green solution in a test tube is probably a poorly separated mixture of pure blue and pure yellow dyes. Similarly, a purple solution is probably unseparated red and blue dyes. Think back to the color wheel in grammar school to decide which primary colors combine to make which secondary colors.

8. Don't be timid in the design of your elution scheme. If one thing doesn't work, completely cleanup the column as described in **Step 6** and start again. Some of the unknown dye mixtures may contain dyes that are more difficult to separate than others. Don't be intimidated by the success or failure of your peers; maybe their unknown mixture has a different dye combination than yours. Experiment! After all, this is the foundation upon which the field of chemistry is built.

Report Sheet—Experiment 15
Chromatography of Artificial Colors

Date _____   **Section number** _____   **Name** _____

Unknown number and initial color_____

List the individual colors (dyes) determined from your elution scheme:

_____

_____

_____

_____

_____

List the solvent mixtures that you used in your longest, most successful elution scheme:

      <u>Example:</u>   <u>60% water/40% methanol</u>

_____

_____

_____

_____

_____

_____

_____

Questions—Experiment 15
Chromatography of Artificial Colors

Date _____   Section number _____   Name _____

1. Which is more polar, methanol or water?

2. What is the relative polarity of the Sep Pak cartridge, polar or nonpolar?

3. Why **are** artificial colors used in consumer products?

4. What would happen to manufacturers' profits if artificial colors were banned in the United States?

5. What are the relative polarities of the dyes encountered in this experiment? List the dyes that you separated (colors) from most polar to least polar. This should be the relative order in which they eluted from your cartridge as you added more and more methanol to your elution mixtures.

Think, Speculate, Reflect, and Ponder

6. Why does the procedure for this experiment suggest beginning the elution scheme with a 100% water solution and adding increasingly more methanol instead of starting with a 100% methanol solution and adding increasingly more water?

7. If the stationary phase in a liquid chromatographic column is made of very polar silica, how can a nonpolar stationary phase be made without using a new stationary phase? (Hint: Try looking in chromatography or quantitative analysis texts.)

Experiment

16

Warning: This Experiment
May Contain Lead

Samples From Home

Bring one or the other of the following to check for lead in paint chips or pottery glaze:

1. A small amount of old paint chips (approximately 0.2 g; if a liquid is used, it must be a water-based solution).

2. If the lead content of a pottery glaze is to be examined, you must bring two liquid samples — at least 100 mL of white distilled vinegar directly from the bottle and an equal 100 mL volume of the same vinegar which has been allowed to sit in an earthenware vessel for 24 hours at room temperature. (Arrangements can also be made to let you carry out your earthenware leaching in the lab beforehand using 5% acetic acid. Check with your lab instructor).

Objectives

A sample from home will be analyzed both qualitatively and quantitatively for lead content. Depending on the sample chosen, quantitative techniques for washing, centrifuging, and otherwise handling small amounts of precipitates will be employed, as well as the opportunity for using a more accurate type of analytical balance. An alternative analysis procedure will use a spectrophotometer which will demonstrate how light can be used as a quantitative tool. These results should permit a valid judgement regarding the safety hazard that a particular sample may pose and whether it exceeds maximum permitted lead concentrations.

Background

Lead (elemental symbol Pb from the Latin *Plumbum*) is a metal that has been known since very ancient times because it is easy to liberate the free metal from its ore. While lead melts at a relatively low temperature, it is a heavy, relatively unreactive element that is used to protect (paints, cable coverings), propel people (car batteries, leaded gasoline), and shoot people (bullets). Its role and effect upon our lives is a mixed blessing, and in this respect it is therefore no different from most chemicals (and political-economic decisions) with which and under which we and the world must live and learn to survive.

It has been only during relatively recent times, however, that human beings have grown in their appreciation and respect for some of the more subtle and insidious problems associated with the use of supposedly "friendly" chemicals. Atoms, of course, are not anthropomorphistic (exhibiting human characteristics) and, therefore, know neither friend nor enemy. Instead, atoms respond only to the laws of nature which human beings, try as we might, cannot alter. Lead is a member of the so-called heavy metal poison club, the full extent and nature of whose toxicities are only now slowly coming to light. You have probably heard of other prominent members—notably mercury (from industrial water pollution, and indiscriminate use of certain fungicides) and its effects on the brain and nervous system. Cadmium (from industrial water pollution leachings from earthenware glazes and iron water pipes), whose alleged implication in heart disease is still to be uncovered, is also in this club.

As with other heavy metals, lead is especially dangerous due to its ability, even in extremely low doses, to accumulate in soft bone in the body much faster than the body can excrete it. Because of this it is termed a cumulative poison, and once present in the body, it is a medically difficult and dangerous job to get rid of it. Some of the more celebrated sources of lead pollution in our environment are large scale air and dust contamination from copper smelters (where lead is often an impurity or minor constituent in the ore) and certainly from the combustion of leaded gasolines. The installation of particle precipitators in smelters' smoke stacks and the introduction of unleaded gasoline for cars have done much to reduce waste lead pollution. The success of these changes can be followed by the precipitous drop in lead dust emissions shown in the table on the following page (abridged from *Stastical Abstracts of the United States*, page 203 (1990); U.S. Department of Commerce, Bureau of the Census):

Lead Emissions (standard tons) in the U.S.

Year	Road Vehicles	Total emissions
1970	172,000 Tons	224,000 Tons
1980	62,000 Tons	78,000 Tons
1987	3,100 Tons	8,900 Tons

Persuasive evidence has appeared supporting the fascinating contribution of lead poisoning to the fall of the Roman Empire. Lead–based plumbing and expensive lead salts for "sweetening" wine—available only to upper class, ruling Romans—may have contributed significant lead doses to their bodies. And similar to those "rich" Romans, there has long been concern that lead solder in water pipes could leach into our water supply. For this reason it is probably advisable to (1) not use water from the hot water line for drinking, and (2) let even the cold water run for a couple of minutes the first time it is turned on each morning. (Newer houses are less likely to suffer from this problem because many were constructed with inert plastic plumbing pipes.)

Many school drinking fountains and faucets today continue to be shut off after discovering that lead concentrations in the water exceed 0.02 ppm—the safe level recommended by the Federal Lead Contamination Act. The U.S. Environmental Protection Agency is aiming to reduce the maximum permitted lead levels in household water supplies from 50 ppb to 15 ppb (parts per billion!).

The Sunday comics do not seem so funny when one realizes that their colored inks also contain lead which can be released into the environment by burning (even putting the ashes on your garden could be inadvisable). There is a good chance that you have read about leaded paints—especially old and peeling—being eaten by children or paint dust being inhaled during housing renovations. Therefore, it is not surprising that according to current federal regulations, all paints manufactured for general public use must now be lead free.

Et Tu, Cadmium *

Owing to its toxicological importance, cadmium frequently has been selected to illustrate the problems of metals pollution. Cadmium is toxic because it inhibits the functioning of some enzyme systems. The gastrointestinal tracts and lungs of humans are particularly susceptible to cadmium poisoning. The average biological half-life for cadmium has been extimated at 17.6 years. Japanese surveys indicate that a daily intake of 200 µg of cadmium increases kidney damage in humans over 50 years of age. Other estimates in Canada and the U.S, indicate that the normal daily intake from conventional foods is about 50 to 80 µg.

* Reprinted with permission from *Chemical & Engineering News* September 8, 38, 1986. Copyright (1986) American Chemical Society.

Finally, there was the discovery (after some unhappy poisonings) that even pottery glazes contain lead which, because of improper firing (heating), can be leached out by food stored in them, especially fruit juices. This dose of lead is thereby passed into the unsuspecting consumer. As monitored and enforced by the U.S. Food and Drug Administration, current (1991) maximum leachable lead levels permitted in earthenware are 0.00025 to 0.0007% (2.5-7 ppm) depending upon the dimensions of the vessel. Acceptable cadmium levels (not measured in this experiment) are only 0.5 ppm. Two test kits for lead available to the public are described in the June 1990 issue of Consumer Reports.

In October 1991 the U.S. Centers for Disease Control lowered the definition for lead poisoning to 10 ppm (parts per million) lead in blood. A child ingesting less than one sugar size granule of lead paint dust each day would reach blood lead levels exceeding this amount. Even though lead in paint is now banned for consumer use, 74% of all private housing built before 1980 contains some lead paint.

Depending upon the nature of and lead concentrations in your sample for this experiment, two qualitative/quantitative procedures are described. The first method determines lead gravimetrically (the weighing of precipitates) and handles lead concentrations of 0.1% or greater in a solid sample. Concentrations down to 0.01% Pb in liquid samples can be detected qualitatively (that is, detected but not measured quantitatively) by this method. The second method determines the amount of lead spectrometrically (in this case how precipitates scatter and block passage of light through a liquid), and it is mainly applicable when lead is present in very small amounts in liquids (0.005 to 0.010% Pb). These are the concentrations that are sometimes found in pottery glaze leach solutions. Your lab instructor can help you decide which method to follow if you are in doubt.

The chemistry of the gravimetric method begins by using nitric acid to decompose your solid sample to dissolve out the lead in the form of lead ions. This lead is then precipitated by adding potassium iodide where the positive lead ions and negative iodide ions combining to form the insoluble lead iodide precipitate as indicated in the chemical reactions:

$$Pb(NO_3)_2 \ + \ 2KI \ \longrightarrow \ 2KNO_3 \ + \ PbI_2$$

| lead (II) nitrate (soluble) | potassium iodide | potassium nitrate (soluble) | lead (II) iodide (insoluble) |

Using an ionic equation, the reactions appears as simply

$$Pb^{+2} \ + \ 2I^{-1} \ \longrightarrow \ PbI_2$$

| lead ions | iodide ions | lead (II) iodide precipitate |

Of the possible metals likely to be present, only lead will form an insoluble iodide salt. Sodium sulfite is added to this solution to reduce unwanted oxidation of the iodide ion by the nitric acid present. If you choose to pursue a quantitative determination at this point, you will wash this precipitate with water to remove any of the soluble compounds sticking to it, and finally with alcohol to wash away the water itself and permit more rapid drying of your precipitate. Such preparation of a sample for accurate weighing is the nature of good and necessary chemical technique.

Since this method will give a yellow PbI_2 precipitate down to 0.01% Pb in your 2 mL of solution, this means that any solid sample containing 0.2 milligram (0.0002g) of lead or more should give a positive test. For a 0.20 g sample, this would mean that a lead concentration as low as 0.1% (1000 ppm) Pb will be detectable.

The alternate spectrometric method precipitates the lead as lead chromate:

$$Pb(NO_3)_2 \ + \ K_2CrO_4 \longrightarrow KNO_3 \ + \ PbCrO_4$$

| lead (II) nitrate (soluble) | potassium chromate (soluble) | potassium nitrate (soluble) | lead (II) chromate (Insoluble yellow precipitate) |

This alternative procedure uses chromate ions: while not so selective for just lead ions as iodide (some other metals besides lead such as barium and copper will also precipitate as chromates), lead chromate is one of the most insoluble of all salts, only 0.0002 g dissolves in a liter of pure water. By contrast, the "insoluble" lead iodide dissolves to the extent of about 0.7 g per liter— still quite insoluble, but nevertheless over 1000 times more soluble than the lead chromate! Chemists understand that soluble and insoluble are only relative terms, and that virtually nothing is completely insoluble in water.

The procedure calls for adding sucrose (sugar) to the solution prior to precipitation. This chemical acts as a stabilizing agent by controlling the growth of precipitating particles. This makes for a smaller and more uniform particle size while retarding the particles from settling out of the solution. In the concentrations used it can also serve to reduce the solubility of the lead chromate still further. Such physical aspects of a precipitate are important when trying to quantitatively measure its amount through the turbidity of the solution using a light beam. That is the function of the Spectronic 20 spectrophotometer, which electronically detects the amount of light passing through your solution. The instrument detects light not scattered or otherwise absorbed along the way by your lead chromate precipitate. For accurate results, your light transmittance data from the lead sample must be compared to that for a nonlead sample so that the final lead concentration can simply be read off from the calibration curve supplied. (Very precise measurements would actually require each person to make his own calibration curve using his own vinegar solution).

Procedure

A. Gravimetric Method (for solid samples like paint chips)

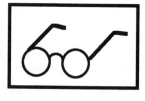

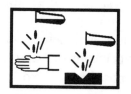

1. Weigh out, to the nearest 0.01 g, about 0.2 g of a solid (or 2.0 g of an aqueous liquid) sample to be tested, and place it into a 3 " (10 x 75 mm) test tube. If a liquid sample is used, add 3 drops of dilute nitric acid and proceed directly to procedure **Step 2(a)**. Otherwise, add 1 mL (about 20 drops) of dilute nitric acid ($6M$ HNO_3) to the solid sample and heat for 15 minutes by placing the test tube into a 100 or 150 mL beaker half full of boiling water. If your sample contains any chunks which do not break up in the acid, use a short solid glass rod to mash them up. Do not lay the rod down on the desk top, but leave it in the test tube.

Most persons can successfully get a positive <u>qualitative</u> test if lead is present, but if you elect to get meaningful results of <u>how much lead</u> is present also, you must try to maintain good quantitative technique. That is what separates the careful, meticulous and successful worker from one who is not successful. The liquid in your test tube contains (we hope) soluble lead ions at this point. You must try not to drop, spill, or otherwise "lose" any of this liquid, some of which is now on your stirring rod, and some of which will shortly be inside a medicine dropper. Chemists avoid losing any sample by both not spilling and by "washing it all out."

2. Go back to your sample heating in the water bath and pull the stirring rod about half way up the inside of the tube and wash it off with 10 drops of distilled water so that the washings fall and mix in with your sample. Set the rod aside. Centrifuge the test tube and contents for a minute (your lab instructor will demonstrate the use for the centrifuge—remember to use a counterweight tube for proper balance).

Using a long-nosed medicine dropper, carefully—technique is important here—transfer as much liquid as you can to a 3 inch test tube (liquid only). If the solids get stirred up, you can always centrifuge again. When you have transferred as much liquid as feasible without sucking up any solid, add ten more drops of distilled water to your test tube containing the solid and repeat the liquid transfer technique of centrifuging and sucking off the liquid with the dropper. Combine the wash liquid with the original solution. When done properly, all of the solid, now washed free of lead ions, will be left in your original tube, while a total of about 2 mL of clear (but possibly colored) liquid containing almost all of your goodies is now in your weighed tube.

(a) Add 1 drop of sodium sulfite solution ($1M$ Na_2SO_3) to your liquid sample. Mix by pressing a small piece of plastic wrap over the tube mouth with your finger and inverting the tube twice. Concentrations of lead much higher than 10% in your original solid sample (or 1% in the larger liquid sample) may result in the formation of a persisting cloudiness at this point, but this will not hurt your results. Add 3 drops of potassium iodide solution ($2M$ KI) and mix well by inverting the test tube as before. What do you observe? A yellow precipitate (not a colored solution) indicates about 0.1% lead or more in your solid sample, or 0.01% or more if you started with two grams of a liquid sample. (If you obtain negative results at this step, add a drop of $0.1M$ $Pb(NO_3)_2$ to the test tube containing the sample to see what a positive test looks like. If your test is positive and you wish to do a quantitative determination, see your instructor for that procedure (extra time needed = 60 minutes).

B. *Spectrometric Method (for vinegar leach samples)*

1. NOTE: All glassware coming into contact with your solutions to be tested must be previously scrubbed with soap and water and then rinsed in distilled water. You should also have with you two white distilled vinegar or 5% acetic acid solutions. One has come "right from the bottle" (label this one <u>blank</u>), while the other has been allowed to stand in some earthenware vessel for 24 hours at room temperature (label this one <u>leach</u>). If either or both of these solutions is not clear of any turbidity, they must be filtered before proceeding further. If any color is present in your leach solutions, they will have to be clarified. See your lab instructor about this.

Pour 35 mL of the blank solution into one 125 mL Erlenmeyer flask, and two 35 mL portions of the leach solution into each of two 125 mL Erlenmeyer flasks. Total = 3 flasks containing 35 mL each—one blank, and two leach. Add to each of these 3 flasks 3.5 g sucrose and swirl the contents of each flask until dissolved.

2. While continuously swirling your blank solution, rapidly add 1.00 mL of potassium chromate ($0.5M$ K_2CrO_4) from a pipette with a pipetter bulb attached. (A type like the "Propipetter" works well; your instructor will indicate the proper and safest technique for using a pipette.) Continue swirling without stopping for 1 minute. (If pipettes are not available, add rapidly, with swirling, 5 drops of $2M$ K_2CrO_4 with a "stubby" medicine dropper.) Repeat this identical procedure with each of the leach solutions and allow the solutions to stand for a least 10 minutes. Note your observations. Any haziness, however faint, in your leach solutions indicates the presence of at least 5 ppm (0.0005%) Pb in your sample.

3. Pour each of your solutions into three separate matched spectrophotometer cuvettes. Your instructor can show you how to "match" cuvette tubes yourself, if necessary. With no sample tube in the Spectronic 20, set the transmittance at 0% with the "zero control" knob. Then wipe the cuvette containing the blank with a tissue and insert it into the sample holder in the top of the instrument so that the vertical mark on the top directly faces you. Close the instrument's cover cap. Check that the wave-length dial is set on 540 millimicrons, mμ (or 540 nanometers, nm)— adjust if necessary now, but do not touch the wavelength knob again throughout the rest of your readings. Using the "light control" knob, adjust until the transmittance reads 100%. (If you are among the first to use the instrument, your instructor will probably have you recheck and read just the zero and percent transmittance settings until the instrument completely warms up.)

(a) Your instrument is now standardized against your pure vinegar or 5% acetic acid reference blank. Remove the blank cuvette and insert the leach cuvette solution into sample holder, wiping and aligning the tube as described before. Record the % transmittance reading. Repeat this procedure with your other duplicate leach solution. Faint cloudiness in the cuvette tube solutions can best be seen visually by looking down on the top of the tube and thus through the whole length of solution while holding the tube against a black background.

(b) Estimate the concentration in parts per million (ppm) of leachable lead in your two leach solutions (10 ppm = 0.001% = 10 mg/L Pb) by referring to the calibration curves on the next page. *Make sure that you use the correct curve for your samples.* The closer your lead values are in the duplicate samples, the more precise you have been in handling both samples in an identical manner.

If you have too much lead in your samples, then the %T will be too low and the lead concentration cannot be read on the curve. In this case, you will have to make a dilution of your leach solution with pure vinegar <u>before</u> testing. If time permits, see your lab instructor regarding how to do this, and what dilution factor to use.

Lead Calibration Curves

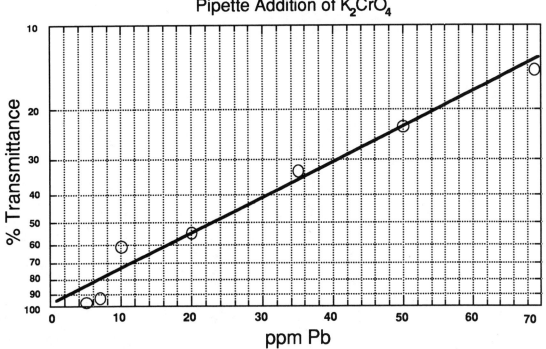

5 % Vinegar Solution
Pipette Addition of K_2CrO_4

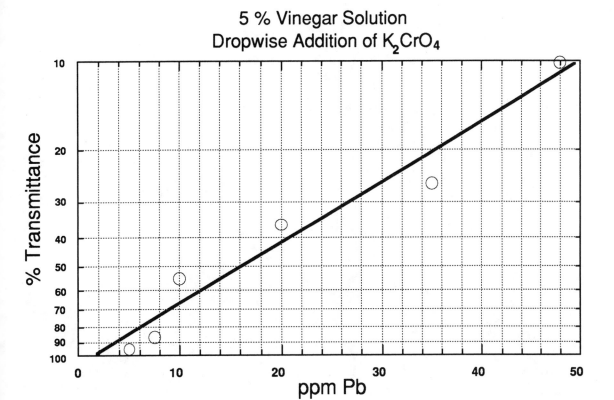

5 % Vinegar Solution
Dropwise Addition of K_2CrO_4

Report Sheet—Experiment 16
Warning: This Experiment May Contain Lead

Date _____   Section number _____   Name _____

A. Gravimetric Method (Paint chip procedure)

1. Sample characteristics

   (a) Nature, brand (if any) and source of sample _____.

   (b) Weight of original sample to nearest 0.01 g   _____g.

2. Observations upon:

   (a) Adding KI solution _____.

   (b) Adding $Pb(NO_3)_2$ if the results in 2(a) were negative _____.

3. Complete only if you performed the quantitative determination of lead:

   (a) Weight of cleaned and dried tube to nearest 0.001 g   _____g.

   (b) Weight of cleaned and dried tube + PbI_2 _____g.

   (c) Calculations:

   (1) Net weight of lead iodide (PbI_2) (subtract line 3(a) from line 3(b)) =

   _____g PbI_2.

   (2) Weight of lead in this amount of lead iodide
   (multiply line 3c(1)) by (0.45 g Pb/g PbI_2) =   _____g Pb.

   (3) % lead in original sample
   (divide line 3c (2) by line 1(b) then multiply by 100 =   _____% Pb.

4. What can you say regarding the safety of your sample in the use for which it is intended?

B. Spectrometric Method (Vinegar leach procedure)

1. Nature of earthenware utensil

    (a) General description _____.

    (b) Country of manufacture, place and date of purchase_____

_____.

2. Observations after adding potassium chromate

    (a) To blank solution _____.

    (b) To leach solutions _____.

    (c) % transmittance of leach sample

        Tube #1_____% T.

        Tube #2_____% T.

4. Concentration in ppm lead in leach samples (from calibration curve)

    Tube #1 _____ppm Pb.

    Tube #2 _____ppm Pb.

    Average = _____ppm Pb.

5. Would your sample pass the FDA standards for lead safety?

C. Comments and conclusions regarding experiment

Questions—Experiment 16
Warning: This Experiment May Contain Lead

Date _____   Section number _____   Name _____

1. Will lead metal dissolve in water?

2. Are there lead compounds which will dissolve in water? If so, cite at least two examples.

3. What is the difference between the "kinds" of lead referred to in Questions #1 and #2?

Think, Speculate, Reflect, and Ponder

4. Which "kind" of lead referred to above in Questions #1 and #2 would you predict to be more toxic? Explain why.

5. List three uses for lead and in each case state why you think lead was chosen rather than some other substance (i.e., what properties does lead have that "endear" it to that particular use?).

   (a)

   (b)

   (c)

6. Why was lead added to gasoline in the first place and then why was it removed?

7. What statement is the artist trying to make in the sketch* below? See this lab's background section for hints.

*Sketch reprinted with permission from *Contemporary Chemistry*, E. A. Walters and E. M. Wewerka, Merrill-MacMillan Publishers. Copyright Edward A. Walters.

Experiment

17

Caffeine Crystals from Beverages

Sample From Home

Bring **one** of the following:

1. One hundred mL of a caffeine containing pop or soft drink*.

2. One hundred mL of a boiling water extract of coffee grounds previously made up to "drinking strength."

3. One hundred mL of a boiling water extract of tea leaves previously made up to "drinking strength."

4. An amount of solid instant tea/coffee sufficient to make about 1/2 cup of drinking liquid (1 g coffee or 1/2 g tea).

* Jolt is advertised as having twice the caffeine as the other caffeinated drinks: Mountain Dew, Sunkist Orange, Mr. Pibb, Tabb, and Shasta among others. Also containing caffeine in lesser amounts are Dr. Pepper, Pepsi, and Royal Crown Cola among others. Noncaffeine pops or soft drinks include 7-UP, Sprite, Fresca, Fanta Orange, RC 100, and most ginger ales. For the caffeine content of specific brands of coffee, tea, and chocolate drinks, see these issues of *Consumer Reports*: September, 1976; October, 1979; May, 1985; and September, 1987.

Objectives

The purpose of this experiment is to isolate and thereby determine the approximate amount of caffeine in some common beverages using an extraction technique. The use of a melting point as a means of identifying substances will also be illustrated.

Background

Caffeine and related compounds are stimulants which are found in a wide variety of plants growing throughout the world. The most common sources are coffee (roasted ground seeds of the coffee shrub), tea (dried leaves of various shrubs found especially in China, Japan, and India), cocoa (roasted ground seeds of the small evergreen cacao tree found in tropical America), maté (a tea-like drink made from the leaves of a species of holly—the national drink in many South American countries), and kola nuts (chestnut sized seeds of a tree indigenous to western tropical Africa, the West Indies and Brazil which are reportedly used in the Sudan both for chewing as well as a form of money). It seems that whenever plants having a high caffeine content grow in particular area, the natives use extracts of the plant as a beverage.

Caffeine

One legend credits the discovery of coffee to a prior (a monastic officer) in an Arabian convent. Shepherds reported to the prior that goats who had eaten the berries of the coffee plant did not rest but gamboled and frisked about all through the night. The prior, mindful of the long nights of prayer which he had to endure, instructed the shepherds to pick the berries so that he might make a beverage from them. The success of his experiment is obvious today!

Although tea leaves contain considerably more caffeine than coffee grounds on a dry weight basis, a cup of coffee will actually contain more caffeine because more coffee than tea is used in brewing a cup that is of drinking strength. Several million pounds of natural (from decaffeinating coffee) and synthetic caffeine are produced annually in the Unites States and are used in headache and "stay-awake" tablets. Because of its stimulant effect on the central nervous system, caffeine has also been used as an antidote to counteract the depressant effects of morphine poisoning. The lethal dose for caffeine in humans is estimated to be about 10 g (10,000 mg), but no deaths have been reported. This lethal dose would be equivalent to around 100 cups of coffee drunk all at once! And for those other questions that you've always wanted to know about caffeine but were afraid to ask, you can now "ask an expert" (see the article after the procedure).

The decaffeinating of coffee used to be done by extracting out the caffeine with liquid chlorinated hydrocarbons—a method similar to the extracting of caffeine from your beverage with methylene chloride in this experiment. Since such chlorinated compounds have been shown to cause liver damage and are implicated as carcinogens, a process using water extraction has now been developed and is widely used. The procedure for this experiment calls for you to dissolve out (to extract) the caffeine from a water solution using the organic solvent methylene chloride, CH_2Cl_2. Caffeine is slightly soluble in water, but very soluble in methylene chloride. Thus mixing these two insoluble liquids together will cause most of the caffeine to preferentially dissolve in the organic (CH_2Cl_2) layer. The sodium carbonate that is added reacts to form salts with many of the noncaffeine substances (especially tannins and tannic acid) and thereby prevents them from also dissolving in the methylene chloride thus contaminating the caffeine. The two liquid layers (water and methylene chloride) are then separated by, in this special case, a rather sneaky kind of filtration. Once wetted with water, the pores of a filter paper will only allow water to drain through them; the methylene chloride layer thus stays in the filter cone while the water layer drains through. The product you get after evaporation of the organic liquid should consist of brown to snow white crystals weighing 15-30 mg.

The question then arises "How do you know that these crystals are indeed caffeine?" The quickest and simplest evidence for identification is obtained by running a melting point determination. Like boiling point and density, the melting point is also a physical constant characteristic for a particular substance. Just as all samples of solid water melt at 0 ° C, all samples of pure caffeine melt at 238 ° C. By comparing the observed melting points of an unknown compound with recorded melting points for known compounds, evidence for identity can be obtained. Your actual observed melting point will probably be a little below 238 ° C, due largely to impurities present in your sample and the unsophisticated design of the melting point apparatus. Caffeine is a material which can sublime (go directly from a solid to a gas phase), so rapid heating of your sample is necessary.

Procedure

A. *Preparation Steps*

Clean a 500 mL Erlenmeyer flask with soap and water. Record the kind of sample and, if it is instant tea or coffee, record its weight. Prepare it for extraction by following *one* of the following three methods:

   a) For carbonated pop or soft drinks—use 100 mL of a cola drink (check the ingredients on the label if in doubt). Pour all of it into a 500 mL Erlenmeyer flask and shake vigorously until the foaming due to carbon dioxide evolution ceases (about 5 minutes).

   b) For instant drinks—weigh out the amount of instant coffee (1 g) or tea (0.5 g) required for 1/2 cup and dissolve this solid in 100 mL of cold water contained in a clean 500 mL Erlenmeyer flask.

   c) For regular brewed drinks—bring to class 100 mL of tea or coffee extract previously made from tea bag, tea leaves, coffee grounds or the like. Pour this 100 mL into a clean 500 mL Erlenmeyer flask.

B. *Isolation Steps*

1. Dissolve roughly two grams of sodium carbonate (Na_2CO_3) in your sample in the 500 mL Erlenmeyer flask prepared in one of the steps of **Part A**.

2. Add 25 mL of CH_2Cl_2 (methylene chloride) and gently agitate by swirling for 5-10 minutes. (Your lab instructor will demonstrate.). DO NOT SHAKE vigorously or a persistent liquid-liquid emulsion will likely form. Coffee samples—especially expresso—must be carefully swirled to avoid obtaining a frothy emulsion.

3. Let the flask contents stand undisturbed for several minutes while you suspend a filter funnel in an iron ring and place a beaker underneath. Fit the funnel with a cone made from a 12 1/2 cm filter paper and wet the paper thoroughly with water. See Experiment 3, *Recycling Aluminum Chemically*, for the proper method of folding the filter paper if you have forgotten.

4. Slowly and carefully pour off and discard as much of the usually dark upper water layer as possible (this is called decantation). Leave in the flask *all* of the organic layer together with some of the remaining water layer.

5. Pour the contents of your 500 mL Erlenmeyer flask (the clear bottom layer of methylene chloride + remaining water) into the previously wetted filter paper cone. Keep the liquid level up near the top of the paper cone until all of the flask contents have been thus transferred. You will see the upper water layer wick into the paper cone and drain through it. Left behind in the filter paper will be the methylene chloride solution containing your dissolved caffeine. (If you have a froth/emulsion in your cone, you may *carefully* and *gently* stir it with a smooth end stirring rod to hasten the separation.)

6. While the last bit of water is draining through the filter cone, take a clean and bone dry 50 mL beaker and put your initials on it (use pencil to write on the frosted glass circle on the side of the beaker). Weigh this beaker to the nearest 0.001 g using a top loading balance and record on the report sheet. (Don't forget to zero the balance.) Your lab instructor can assist you in the use and care of these balances. (Be warned that these balances will quickly spoil you so that you will want to use nothing else!)

7. Using a medicine dropper, transfer to the weighed beaker ONLY the clear methylene chloride layer remaining in your filter cone. (If desired, your lab instructor can help you clarify any brown coloration in the methylene chloride layer.) And if any water droplets can been seen contaminating your methylene chloride solution, your lab instructor can show you how to remove them also, using anhydrous sodium sulfate.

8. Go to the hood and place your beaker on a hot plate, but DO NOT LEAVE BEAKER UNATTENDED. Avoid breathing the methylene chloride vapors. Watch the liquid contents closely and when the liquid level in the beaker gets down to about 1/16 of an inch IMMEDIATELY REMOVE the beaker from the hot plate and set it in the hood to cool while the small remainder of methylene chloride liquid evaporates (5 minutes).

Observe and record your observations and make a sketch of the solid residue in the beaker with the aid of a microscope. Reweigh the beaker to the nearest 0.001 g. (Be sure to use the same balance that you used before.) Using a spatula, divide your sample into two approximately equal piles. Taste a small amount from one pile (optional) and record your response on the report sheet. Use the other pile in the melting point determination which follows.

C. *Melting Point Determination*

You only get one chance to take a melting point, so read this section through carefully before beginning.

The melting point apparatus is diagrammed in Figure 17.1. Be sure to use a cork (not a rubber stopper) having a hole that *snugly* holds a thermometer (250 ° or higher). Clamp the 8 inch test tube horizontally about six inches above your desk top and insert the cork + thermometer to make sure everything fits properly. Then carefully transfer the remaining pile of caffeine onto the bulb of your thermometer with a spatula and gently reinsert the thermometer into the test tube. Be careful to keep the caffeine sample on top of the bulb.

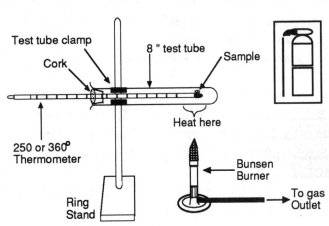

Figure 17.1. *Set-up for melting point determination.*

If you have thought, as well as read, ahead, the numbered scale on the thermometer will be facing you for easy reading. Adjust a lit Bunsen burner to give a cooler flame by cutting down somewhat on the air supply (remember Experiment 1, *The Ubiquitous Bunsen Burner*). No inner hot cone should be present.

Proceed to heat the bottom of the test tube with the flame, moving it back and forth directly under the thermometer bulb. Watch the caffeine crystals closely. The crystals will first collapse to form an opaque semisolid mass. Record as the melting point the temperature at which this mass suddenly turns water clear or tannish-clear. Let your apparatus cool and then disassemble and clean the thermometer bulb.

With the aid of a microscope, observe and comment on the white "fog" coating the inside of your 8 inch test tube. (Hint: Place the "fog" side of the test tube "up" under the microscope. Touch a pencil tip to the top of the tube and focus on the pencil tip to locate the proper focus height for the scope to see the "fog".)

How Much Caffeine Is Too Much? *

Question: What can you tell me about caffeine in the diet? How much is too much? Are the new extra caffeine soft drinks like "Jolt" damaging? I've read that caffeine has been found to speed weight loss by speeding up the body's metabolism. Is that true? Also, is there a difference in the caffeine in coffee, tea or soft drinks? I've also heard that caffeine has been linked to a high incidence of breast cysts in women.

Answer (from Maureen Raskin, GHC nutritionist and chronic disease epidemiologist): Caffeine is one of a group of compounds known as methyl-xanthines found in a wide variety of substances—from over-the-counter medications to foods where it occurs naturally. It may be present in headache, cold, allergy, menstrual pain and general pain-killing over-the-counter remedies as well as in diet pills, stay-awake pills and some prescription drugs. It is found naturally in coffee and tea, and in smaller amounts in chocolate and cocoa. The amount of caffeine in coffee and tea depends on how the beverage is prepared and which brands are used. I have included a summary table so you may make some comparisons.

Since there is no strong evidence that moderate amounts of caffeine are harmful to the *average healthy* adult, it is listed on the "Generally Regarded as Safe" [GRAS] list put out by the U.S. Food & Drug Administration. The Food Chemicals Codex of the U.S. National Academy of Sciences/National Research Council lists caffeine as a flavoring agent and stimulant.

Excessive consumption is considered to be more than 600 mg. per day (about 5-6 cups of strongly brewed coffee). However, individual tolerance to caffeine varies considerably. Persons who generally consume little or no caffeine show much greater sensitivity to it than those who consume caffeine on a regular basis. Symptoms of excess caffeine intake (known as caffeinism) can include anxiety, restlessness, delayed onset of sleep, headache, diarrhea and heart palpitations.

Caffeine exerts several effects on the body even when consumed in safe amounts. It stimulates the central nervous system, thereby producing the "lift" so many people seek. Depending on the dose, it can increase heartbeat, increase secretion of stomach acid, and yes, it can also increase one's resting metabolic rate. I do not recommend it for persons who are prone to stomach ulcers or for persons with diabetes since it tends to keep one's blood sugar elevated for a longer period of time after a meal. This last effect is why it is used in weight control products as a means to assist in reducing the feeling of hunger. Caffeine is used in many headache remedies, in combination with other drugs, because it constricts the swollen blood vessels in the head that cause headache and so helps speed relief.

The time required for the body to eliminate caffeine varies from several hours to several days, depending upon age, if other medications are being used, and whether or not the individual smokes. The amount of time needed for the body to get rid of half the caffeine consumed (scientists call this the "half life" of a substance) is as follows: for children and smokers it is less than 3 hours, for the average nonsmoking adult, about 5 to 7 hours; for women taking oral contraceptives, up to 13 hours; for pregnant women on their last trimester, 18 to 20 hours; and for newborns (who do not have the enzymes needed to metabolize caffeine until several days after birth), 3 to 4 days. Caffeine crosses the placenta so pregnant women are giving it to the fetus, and it is secreted into human milk.

Several studies have been done which suggested an association between consumption of methylxanthines (caffeine and its close relative, theobromine) and fibrocystic breast disease (FBD). The amount of benefit gained from abstaining from caffeine remains unclear. While modest results were obtained from some studies, the largest study conducted by researchers from the National Cancer Institute failed to support such findings. Perhaps this is yet another example of the wide variation in individual response—limiting or avoiding caffeine may be helpful for some women yet of no value in reducing symptoms of FBD in other women. I guess like just about everything else, the word is "moderation."

Item	mg. of Caffeine
Coffee (5oz.)	
Drip	110-150
Percolated	64-124
Instant	40-108
Decaffeinated	2-5
Tea (5 oz.)	
1-minute brew	9-33
3-minute brew	20-46
5-minute brew	20-50
Chocolate Products	
Hot Coca (6 oz.)	2-8
Chocolate Milk (8 oz.)	2-7
Milk Chocolate (1 oz.)	1-15
Sweet Dark Chocolate (1 oz.)	5-35
Soft Drinks [†]	
Jolt	72
Mountain Dew	54
Tab	47
Coca-Cola	46
Shasta Cola	44
Dr. Pepper	40
Pepsi Cola	38
RC Cola	36

Product	mg. per Tablet/Capsule
Vivarin Tablets	200
No-Doz Tablets	100
Dexatrim ¥	200
Diatac ¥	200
Exedrin	65
Vanquish	33
Anacin	32
Midol	32
Plain aspirin, any brand	0

¥ These products also come in caffeine-free versions.

[†]Colas and pepper-type drinks derive less than 5% of their total caffeine content for the cola nut. The rest is added and typically is the caffeine obtained from raw coffee beans in the process of decaffeinating coffee.

* Taken from *View Magazine*, January/February 1988, page 28. Copyright 1988, Group Health Cooperative; reprinted by permission of the publisher.

Report Sheet—Experiment 17
Caffeine

Date _____   Section number _____   Name _____

1. Isolation of caffeine

Nature of sample (beverage type, brand) _____.

Amount of sample taken _____.

Appearance of solid residue in beaker after evaporation of methylene chloride _____.

Sketch of caffeine crystals

2. Examination of caffeine

Weight of beaker + dry residue of caffeine
_____grams.

Weight of beaker (empty and dry)   _____grams.

Total weight of residue only   _____grams caffeine.

Taste of the residue (optional) _____.

Melting point of residue   _____ °C.

Melting point of pure caffeine (consult *The Merck Index.*)   _____ °C.

Description of coating on 8 inch test tube _____

_____.

3. Comments and conclusions on experiment

Questions—Experiment 17
Caffeine

Date _____   **Section number** _____   **Name** _____

1. In the caffeine isolation steps

    (a) Which layer in the actual extraction step was the methylene chloride—the top or the bottom?

    (b) What physical property of methylene chloride would cause it to be the particular layer that you said it was in (a) above?

2. A thin film of white solid can often be seen on the cooler parts of the test tube and on the thermometer inside the apparatus after completing the melting point determination. What is this solid and how did it get there?

3. At what temperature does caffeine start to sublime rapidly? (HINT: Check *The Merck Index*.)

4. Give the brand name and ingredient list of two drugs that contain caffeine.

    (a)

    (b)

Think, Speculate, Reflect, and Ponder

5. The symptoms of withdrawal from an addicting drug are irritability, desire for the addicting drug, and physical discomfort. All of these symptoms are relieved by a dose of the addicting drug. Using this as an indicator, is caffeine an addicting drug?

6. Do other extremely widely used drugs like alcohol and the nicotine in cigarettes fit the profile of addicting drugs? State one reason why you would (or would not) favor a law making the sale of one or both of these drugs illegal.

Experiment

18

Fluoridation
What—Another Plot to Poison Us?

Sample From Home

Bring a small (5 mL) sample of clear water from the tap or some natural source.

Objectives

In this experiment you will determine the fluoride content of a water sample using a standardized procedure. You will be able to compare your results with the fluoride limits set by your local public health department.

Background

"...*The main communist plots by the internal traitors in the U.S. are fluoridation, disarmament and federal aid to education...This (fluoridation) will positively degenerate Christian Americans by dulling their brain and crippling their bodies. Fluoridation causes an increase of 30% to 125% in anemia, diabetes, heart disease, stroke and cancer; fluoridation also causes abortions and mongoloid births. Do you want your children to become progressively dull and morons? Do you want your grandchildren to be born mongoloids and cripples? Then get out and fight fluoridation day and night."*

Such ringing rhetoric rode the crest of a wave of anti-intellectualism in the scare campaign against fluoridation in the mid 1960s, receiving wide support from such well known organizations as the Ku Klux Klan and the John Birch Society. Ever since 1941, when a group of dentists in Wisconsin proposed the fluoridation of public water supplies to reduce tooth decay, the battle was joined and still rages today.

As approved and recommended by the United States Public Health Service, water fluoridation involves adding fluoride to the water supply until the concentration level falls within limits set in the following table. The permitted amounts are tied to temperature because of its effect upon water consumption.

Annual Average of Maximum Daily Air Temperatures (deg. F)	Recommended Control Limits of Fluoride Concentration (ppm)		
	Lower	Optimum	Upper
50.0-53.7	0.9	1.2	1.7
53.8-58.3	0.8	1.1	1.5
58.4-63.8	0.8	1.0	1.3
63.9-70.6	0.7	0.9	1.2
70.7-79.2	0.7	0.8	1.0
79.3-90.5	0.6	0.7	0.8

The actual fluoridation chemicals used, in order of decreasing cost, are fluosilicic acid (a liquid), sodium fluoride, ammonium silicofluoride, sodium silicofluoride, and fluorspar. In large cities, the annual cost per person amounts to around thirty cents. The addition of the controlled amounts of fluoride indicated in this table has been shown to reduce tooth decay 60–65% at age 15 if children consume fluoridated water from time of birth, and continued inhibition carries on into adult life.

Strangely, persons who are against fluoridation often seem willing to accept the necessity for *chlorination* of water supplies—in spite of the fact that free elemental chlorine is not found naturally in any substance on earth. Neither are some of the reaction products of chlorine with water or with water pollutants found naturally in any water supply—some of which are suspected of being possible carcinogens. Fluorides, on the other hand, are one of many trace ions naturally present in water and foods and, like many other elements, actually appear to be necessary in small amounts for good health—much like iodide which is required to prevent the development of the condition known as goiter. The table on the next page lists some typical natural fluoride concentrations in foods (*Public Health Reports* 64, 1061 (1949)). Since most fluorine in food is organically bound, only about 50% may be taken in by the body as fluoride ions.

Fluoride Content of Foods

Food	Fluorine (ppm)	Food	Fluorine (ppm)
Fluorine reported in food as consumed			
Milk	0.07-0.22	Pork Chop	1.00
Egg White	0.00-0.60	Frankfurters	1.70
Egg Yolk	0.40-2.00	Round Steak	1.30
Butter	1.5	Oysters	1.50
Cheese	1.6	Herring (smoked)	3.50
Beef	< 0.20	Canned Shrimp	4.40
Liver	1.50-1.60	Canned Sardines	7.30-12.50
Veal	0.20	Canned Salmon	8.50-9.00
Mutton	< 0.20	Fresh Fish	1.60-7.00
Chicken	1.4	Canned Mackerel	26.89
Pork	< 0.20		
Fluorine reported in dry substance of food			
Rice	< 1.00	Honey	1.00
Corn	< 1.00	Cocoa	0.50-2.00
Corn (canned)	< 0.20	Milk Chocolate	0.50-2.00
Oats	1.30	Chocolate (plain)	0.50
Crushed Oats	< 0.20	Tea (various brands)	30.00-60.00
Dried Beans	0.20	Cabbage	0.31-0.50
Whole Buckwheat	1.70	Lettuce	0.60-0.80
Wheat Bran	< 1.00	Spinach	1.00
Whole Wheat Flour	1.30	Tomatoes	0.60-0.90
Biscuit Flour	0.00	Turnips	< 0.20
Flour	1.10-1.20	Carrots	< 0.20
White Bread	1.00	Potato (white)	< 0.20
Ginger Biscuits	2.00	Potato (sweet)	< 0.20
Rye Bread	5.30	Apples	0.80
Gelatin	0.00	Pineapple (canned)	0.00
Dextrose	0.50	Orange	0.22

Interestingly, tea is exceptional in its ability to concentrate fluoride, and some special teas have been reported to contain as much as 1530 ppm fluoride on a dry basis. In fact, tea is a major source of fluoride in the tea-drinking New Zealanders' diet because their drinking water is practically free of this element. In many parts of the world, the natural fluoride concentration is well in excess of 1.0 ppm. The largest area of high fluoride concentration in the United States is in the panhandle/West Texas region where such concentrations average 3–6 ppm and have stood at 8.0 ppm in Bartlett, Texas since at least as far back as 1901. Studies have shown that similar population groups in other countries, including the U.S.S.R., have been drinking high concentrations of fluoride for generations. Extensive medical examination showed the high fluoride levels to have had no adverse action on the health of the affected population when compared to a control population sample nearby, which would be subjected to similar environmental stresses except for having a very low fluoride level in its drinking water. The main undesirable effect— and one which is consistently noted with high (over 2 ppm) fluoride content of drinking water— is principally a cosmetic one due to mottling of the teeth to give a brown stained appearance. The following two tables graphically illustrate the effects of fluoridated water upon tooth mottling (*Fluorine Chemistry*, IV, 449 (1965) by H. C. Hodge and F. A. Smith; copyright Academic Press; reprinted with permission) and tooth mortality (*Public Health Reports*, 66, 1389 (1951) by A. L. Russell and E. Elvove; reprinted with permission). Drinking water in Colorado Springs, CO has contained 2.0–2.5 ppm fluoride since at least the turn of this century, whereas the concentration in Boulder, CO water, about 100 miles away, is only 0.0–0.1 ppm.

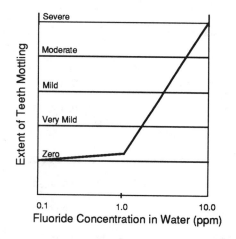
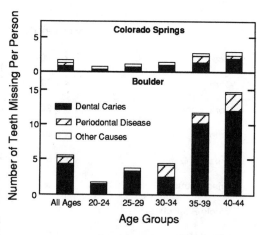

Threshold levels for optimum tooth protection begin around 0.7 ppm fluoride. Sea water ranges from 1.0–1.4 ppm fluoride and almost all the world's fresh water drinking supplies contain over 0.05 ppm fluoride largely due to the leaching of this element from certain rocks such as calcium fluoride (commonly called fluorspar or fluorite). About 10.5 million Americans have been drinking water containing such natural fluoride at concentrations over 0.7 ppm for generations. Other water supplies have had fluoride added to bring up the concentration to optimum levels (near 1.0 ppm). The government's objective has long been to have 95% of the population drinking fluoridated water by 1990. As of October 1986, however., the total was only 129 million or 54%.

Fluoridation of public drinking water was first begun in the United States in 1945. Undoubtedly due largely to the ability to study the long term effects of high fluoride concentrations on a relatively large number of people, most authorities have been convinced as to not only its safety, but its desirability except for persons using an artificial kidney. But now an increasing number of professionals are feeling that perhaps continued fluoridation, at least in the United States, is unnecessary due to the availability and widespread use of fluoridated toothpastes. Serious questions are also being raised about a possible role of fluoride in some bone disease. But the following quote in a letter appearing in *Chemical and Engineering News* (March 26, page 3 (1990); reprinted with permission of Margaret M. Gemperline) does much to put the debate in perspective: "I watched, chagrined, as my husband, who is a Ph.D. chemist, lavished fluoride toothpaste on my son's toothbrush and my son gleefully swallowed every bit of it. I have only a M. S. degree in chemistry, but I managed to convince my husband to skimp on the toothpaste until I could obtain a tube of ingestible toothpaste containing no fluoride. I am less worried about water fluoridated at 1 ppm than I am about young children swallowing toothpaste with fluoride at levels of 1000 ppm."

Most major developed countries do not fluoridate their water supplies. The adjacent table (reprinted with permission from *Chemical and Engineering News*, August 1, page 30 (1988); Copyright (1988) American Chemical Society) shows the prevalence of fluoridation in different countries of the world including a few (formerly) communist nations where it was perhaps termed by some a "capitalist plot."

For many years a good sensitive analytical procedure which could detect fluoride ions in low concentrations did not exist. There are now two official procedures accepted for fluoride analysis by the U.S. Geological Survey and departments of public health. One uses what are called ion specific electrodes which can electronically and quickly measure the F-concentration. This method is the one most often used now, but the apparatus is rather expensive. The other method—an adaptation of which this experiment follows—was developed in 1954 and determines the amount of fluoride ion by mixing the sample with a red-colored complex ion formed by reaction of an organic dye (eriochrome cyanine R) with zirconium ions. (This constitutes the "mixed indicator solution" used in the experiment). This rather exotic red zirconium/dye complex ion is chosen

Fluoridation World Wide

Country	Population (millions)	Percent of Population Drinking Artificially Fluoridated Water
Albania	3.1	0 %
Australia	16.1	66
Austria	7.6	0
Belgium[a]	9.9	0
Bulgaria	9.0	0
Canada	25.9	50
Czechoslovakia	15.6	20
Denmark	5.1	0
East Germany[e]	16.6	9
Finland[b]	4.8	1.5
France	55.6	0
Greece	10.0	0
Hungary	10.6	0
Ireland	3.5	50
Italy	57.4	0
Japan	122.0	0
Luxembourg	0.4	0
Netherlands[c]	14.6	0
New Zealand	3.3	66
Norway	4.2	0
Poland	37.7	4
Portugal[a]	10.3	0
Romania	22.9	0
Spain	39.0	< 1 %
Sweden	8.4	0
Switzerland	6.6	4
United Kingdom	56.8	9
United States	243.8	50
U. S. S. R. (pre 1991)	284.0	15
West Germany[d,e]	61.0	0
Yugoslavia	23.4	0

[a] One experimental treatment plant now discontinued.
[b] One small experimental treatment plant. [c] Discontinued in 1976 after 23 years of experiments. [d] Discontinued in 1978 after 18 years of experiments. [e] Before German reunification in 1990.

because fluoride ions react with it to displace some of the zirconium ions from the organic complex which causes a loss of some of the red color. Thus the redder the complex remains after the water sample is added to it, the less fluoride is present; while the more pale it becomes, the more fluoride there is present. Tin chloride is added to inactivate any chromate, residual chlorine, or other similar oxidizing agents which, if present, would interfere with the result. The intensity of this red color will be measured electronically with a Spectronic 20 spectrophotometer, whose principle and method of operation were described in Experiment 16, *Warning: This Lab May Contain Lead*. Comparison of the observed light absorbance of your sample with a calibration curve will permit you to directly read the concentration of fluoride in your unknown water sample. Although absorbance numbers are harder to read off the Spectronic 20 than % transmittance, the absorbance is directly proportional to color concentration. Thus the plot of F-concentration against absorbance gives a straight line graph.

Procedure

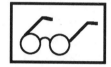

Although this analysis involves very few steps, a high degree of meticulousness will be required of you in order to get accurate results. In order to check your accuracy and maximize the validity of your results, this procedure has you run the unknown water samples in duplicate.

1. Scrupulously clean two 4 inch test tubes with soap and water and rinse thoroughly with distilled water. In order to completely dry your test tubes, heat each tube separately in the blue flame of a Bunsen burner by holding one tube at a time with your wire test tube holder and passing it through the burner's flame until it is completely dry. Obtain a 2 mL pipette and, using a pipette bulb, suck some distilled water up into the pipette and allow to drain out. If the pipette is clean, no water droplets will remain clinging to the inside of the pipette. The presence of such droplets means that the pipette is dirty (however clean it may look!) and should be washed and rinsed with distilled water before use.

2. Now that your necessary equipment is clean, you can proceed to test for traces of fluoride ion in your water sample from home. Your water sample must be absolutely clean and free of sediment—if not, see your lab instructor. Flush out the 2 mL pipette with your water sample and transfer exactly 2.00 mL of unknown water to each of your two clean and dry 4 inch test tubes. Using the medicine dropper provided in the reagent bottle, add exactly one drop of stannous (tin) chloride solution to each of the two samples (let it fall from the dropper tip with a steady hand). Mix by agitating from side-to-side (bounce back and forth between your fingers) and let stand for ten minutes. (Your lab instructor may elect to dispense the following reagent instead of having you follow the procedure in **Step 3**.)

3. Go to where the mixed indicator reagent is located and, using the burette or pipette set up for this purpose, add exactly 5 mL of this reagent to each of your two samples. The pipette uses the same automatic pipetter bulb seen in Experiment 13, *Vitamin C in Your Diet*. Your lab instructor can again assist in showing you how it works. After the mixed indicator reagent has been added, place a small piece of plastic wrap over the mouth of each tube, mix well by inverting the contents several times, and allow the test tubes to stand for a minimum of 30 minutes.

4. Carefully scrutinize the light red-orange solutions in your tubes by holding them up to the light. A better way is to look down on top of the solutions and thence down through the whole depth of solution in the tube against a black background (again, described in Experiment 16, *Warning: This Lab May Contain Lead*). If *any* haze or cloudiness at all is discernible, you must proceed to **Step 5** and separate it from the solution by centrifugation before measuring the absorbance of your solutions with the spectrophotometer. Water samples low in sulfate ion concentration will probably not give such cloudiness, in   which case you can proceed directly to **Step 6**. Note the presence or absence of any such haziness on the report sheet.

5. (PERFORM THIS STEP ONLY IF YOUR SAMPLES ARE CLOUDY) If centrifuges are available which can accommodate the 4 inch tubes, spin them for 5 minutes (your lab instructor will demonstrate). If only the smaller 3 inch capacity centrifuges are available, proceed as follows: First clean and dry four 3 inch test tubes in the same manner as you did the 4 inch tubes back in
Step 1. Number them in pairs, for instance, AA and BB and transfer your two red-orange solutions into these two pairs by pouring the solution from the 4 inch test tube into the 3 inch test tubes. Divide up each sample as equally as possible between each pair of two 3 inch tubes. Place the two pairs (4 tubes total) into a centrifuge opposite each other and spin them for at least five minutes.

Obtain two cuvette tubes rinsed in distilled water but not necessarily dry. Be careful with them as they are expensive. Using a clean, dry capillary pipette (long nose medicine dropper) carefully suck up some of the clear liquid from one four inch tube (or one pair of 3 inch centrifuge tubes) and squirt about 1 mL (20 drops) into a cuvette tube. Agitate the liquid around in the tube and discard. (This serves to wash the tube free of distilled water.) Fill the cuvette about two-thirds full with the remainder of the now clear liquid. Be careful not to suck up any sediment. If you accidentally stir up the sediment on the bottom of a centrifuge tube, spin it down again for another 5 minutes.

Repeat this transfer technique with your duplicate sample in the other 4 inch tube (or pair of 3 inch centrifuge tubes). You are now ready to use the spectrophotometer: proceed directly to **Step 7**.

6. Obtain two cuvette tubes rinsed in distilled water but not necessarily dry. Be careful with them as they are expensive. Using a clean, dry capillary pipette (long nose medicine dropper) squirt about 1 mL (20 drops) in one of your 4 inch test tubes from **Step 4** into a cuvette tube. Agitate the liquid around in the tube and discard the liquid. (This serves to wash the tube free of distilled water.). Fill the cuvette about two-thirds full with the remainder of the solution left in the 4 inch test tube.

Repeat this transfer technique with your duplicate sample in the other 4 inch test tube. You are now ready to use the spectrophotometer in the next step.

7. Refer to Experiment 16, *Warning: This Lab May Contain Lead*, for a description of the operation of the Spectronic 20. Set the wavelength dial at 540 mµ. After adjusting the zero control knob, insert the provided cuvette containing *the reference blank solution* (2 mL of distilled water + 1 drop stannous chloride solution + 5 mL mixed indicator solution) into the machine and set the needle to read 0.500 *absorbance*. Remember to handle the cuvette tubes by the top and to wipe them clean and dry on the outside with tissue before inserting them into the instrument. Insert the two cuvettes containing your duplicate water samples and record the absorbance of each on the report sheet. Remember to align the vertical mark at the top of the tube so that it faces you and close the instrument cuvette cover cap before taking your reading. Examine the lower absorbance scale carefully to be certain you read it correctly. Note that the value of each division changes in different parts of the scale. (Absorption is actually a logarithmic scale.) When you are finished, wash out the two cuvettes containing your samples thoroughly with distilled water and place them into a cuvette rack in an inverted position.

Reasonably precise absorbance readings should lie within 0.01 absorbance units of each other. If your two values deviate from each other by much more than this, your experimental technique was probably not done so carefully as it should or could have been. Read off the actual fluoride ion concentration of your unknown water sample to the nearest 0.1 ppm from a calibration curve and compare it with values, if any, obtained from your public health department. (See your lab instructor for the calibration curve.)

This procedure will accurately handle fluoride ion concentrations up to around 3 ppm. Observed absorbances of less than 0.10 indicate that you may have a sample containing more than 3 ppm F-. In such cases the best accuracy can be obtained either by making a prior dilution of your water sample (necessitating repeating the experiment) or changing the absorbance setting of the reference blank solution to a higher value (0.600 or 0.700 absorbance) and running a new calibration curve. See your lab instructor for help with this.

Report Sheet—Experiment 18
Fluoridation

Date _____   **Section number** _____   **Name** _____

1. Water Sample

    (a) Nature and source of water sample _____.

    (b) Geographical location where sample taken _____.

    (c) Water district (if tap water used) _____.

2. Appearance of solutions after adding mixed indicator reagent:

3. Spectrophotometer Data

Tube	Absorbance Readings	ppm Fluoride Concentration (from curve)
1		
2		
3 (Optional)		
Reference Blank	0.500	0.0

4. Fluoride analysis

    (a) Average of fluoride concentrations above _____.

    (b) Reported fluoride level
    (Check with water department or public health department.) _____.

    (c) Recommended optimum fluoride concentration
    (see table in background) _____.

5. Comments and conclusions on experiment

Questions—Experiment 18
Fluoridation

Date _____   Section number _____   Name _____

1. Data handling

(a) What would be the difference between the precision of your results and their accuracy?

(b) Is the accuracy or precision of your data better?

2. Bottles of sodium fluoride have a skull and crossbones emblem on them to warn that the substance is a dangerous poison, and it is sometimes used as an rodenticide. However, sodium fluoride is also added to public drinking water. Explain.

3. Name two common everyday man-made materials that most people use which contain fluorine. (Consult the index in a chemistry text, if necessary, for help.)

Think, Speculate, Reflect, and Ponder

4. Foods contain much of their fluorine in combination with carbon compounds. Explain how this "organic" fluorine differs from ionic fluorine like that in sodium fluoride. (Hint: What type of bond would hold fluorine to carbon atoms?)

Experiment

19

Sunglasses, Ultraviolet Radiation, and You

Sample From Home

Bring at least one pair of sunglasses to lab for this experiment. Get as much information about that pair of glasses as possible. The cost, manufacturer, and any ultraviolet and infrared light blocking claims by the manufacturer are all relevant to this experiment.

Objectives

The purpose of this experiment is to allow you to measure the light blocking ability of your sunglasses. To do this you will watch the lab instructor operate a scanning spectrophotometer. The data that you will collect for each pair of glasses will give you information about their ultraviolet, infrared, and visible light transmission (or absorption) characteristics and even allow you to speculate about the visible spectrum of any colored lens.

Background

The radiation bathing the earth from our sun has a very wide spectral range. This means that the incoming light is made up of many different wavelengths (colors). Included in this life-giving radiation, however, are wavelengths of light that are harmful to organisms on the surface of the earth. Specifically, light in the ultraviolet region of the solar spectrum can be damaging to many organisms including human beings. Fortunately, our environment provides protection for the organisms that might be exposed to this harmful radiation.

The atmosphere above the earth acts as a radiation filter in such a way as to remove significant amounts of ultraviolet radiation *before it strikes the earth*. The important chemical member of this atmospheric filter is *ozone* (O_3). Ozone is involved in a continuous cycle of creation and destruction in the upper atmosphere called the Chapman Cycle (or mechanism) that also involves O_2 molecules and O atoms. The net result of the Chapman Cycle is the transformation of incoming energy in the ultraviolet wavelength into energy in the infrared wavelength which prevents most of this ultraviolet radiation from reaching the surface of the earth. This process occurs far above the surface of the earth and at a safe distance above plants and animals that can be damaged by ultraviolet radiation. It also acts to heat the upper regions of the stratosphere causing a natural temperature inversion there, but that is another story. Let's concentrate on the ozone layer.

The protective layer of ozone has been present in our upper atmosphere for millions of years. It is maintained, like many other atmospheric chemical cycles, by dynamic processes that involve both gases already in the upper atmosphere and those diffusing upward from the surface of the earth. In the 1930s, scientists at the Du Pont Company synthesized a family of chemicals called chlorofluoro-carbons (CFC's). These inert molecules were originally synthesized to be used in refrigeration as a replacement for the toxic chemicals then in use such as ammonia and sulfur dioxide. Due to their inertness, CFC's do not react

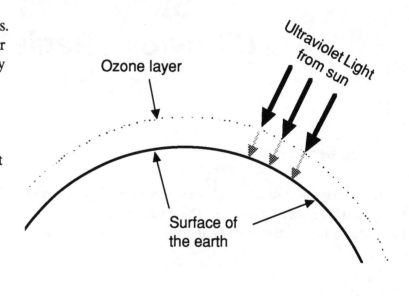

Figure 19.1. *Simplified representation of UV filtering by the earth's ozone layer.*

to any appreciable degree with light or with chemicals that they encounter in the lower atmosphere (where we release them, as you will soon learn). They were very well designed for their job as refrigerants and in fact can be breathed by human beings with no danger. (Compare this to ammonia or sulfur dioxide, which are both toxic and stinkers besides!) After the Second World War this property of chemical inertness made this class of compounds very useful in a variety of industrial applications beyond refrigeration such as cleaning agents and foam blowing agents, and therefore they provided our society with many benefits while greatly expanding their use even further than before.

Since their introduction, these totally synthetic molecules have been escaping from their containers. They get loose in the lower atmosphere due to human beings: We release them on purpose or by accident from our air conditioners, refrigerators, solvent baths, etc. Since they don't react in the lower atmosphere, they become uniformly mixed in the lower atmosphere and slowly diffuse upward through the atmosphere. The average transit time for these compounds from the surface of the earth to the upper atmosphere has been estimated to be between one and two decades. This means that the chlorofluorocarbons released in the late 1960s and 1970s are just now arriving and causing problems in the ozone layer. Causing problems? But aren't they inert? Read on.

When CFC's finally arrive in the upper atmosphere (in a region called the stratosphere), their inertness becomes a thing of the past. The incoming solar radiation at that altitude is of sufficient energy to break apart these molecules and free their previously strongly bound chlorine atoms (all of the original *chloro*fluorocarbons had some chlorine atoms). The newly freed chlorine atoms are the real culprits in the destruction of ozone in the stratosphere. Each chlorine atom takes part in a cycle of ozone destruction that destroys tens of thousands of ozone molecules before that particular chlorine atom is removed or converted to an atmospherically inert chlorine reservoir species. This means that the chlorine atoms contributed to the stratosphere from CFC's are very effective catalysts for ozone destruction. But what happens as the ozone layer thins?

The amount of ultraviolet (UV) radiation that strikes the earth under the ozone layer has *never* been zero since the ozone layer is not completely opaque to UV rays; some UV has always made it through. And, indeed, some UV exposure is required to initiate the production of vitamin D in human beings and probably also plays a role in genetic changes (on an evolutionary time scale); however, as the ability of the ozone layer to block UV decreases (because of ozone depletion due to CFC's), the amount of UV radiation striking the earth is increasing. The effects of increased surface UV radiation upon human beings is well documented: more UV means more skin cancers and more eye cataracts for human beings. The effects on crops, ocean algae, and animals is not as well understood but may also be quite damaging.

As the UV radiation striking the earth increases, we will have to take more stringent precautions against this danger. In the past we have protected our eyes from dangerous UV radiation by the use of UV blocking sunglasses, and we have protected our skin by using UV opaque sunscreen lotions. Sunglasses are designed to selectively block some wavelengths of light while allowing other wavelengths to pass through the lens and into your eye. Since there is no informational benefit in allowing UV into your eyes (since UV is invisible to our eyes and therefore can not help you *see* something), it is desirable that all ultraviolet radiation be blocked by sunglasses.

Visible colors, however, can be selectively filtered by sunglasses to benefit the wearers in the particular light situation that they are in. For instance, dark mirrored sunglasses help the mid-day, full-sun skier who is skiing at high altitudes. Relatively light-colored, yellow sunglasses aid a skier in fog or blizzard conditions. Good skiers carry both in case the conditions change quickly.

Procedure

This experiment is designed to allow you to measure the light filtering ability of a pair of your own sunglasses. To accomplish this you will use (actually, watch you lab instructor operate) an instrument that measures both the wavelength and intensity of light that passes through your sunglasses. This instrument sends a beam of light through the sample (your sunglasses) and measures what comes through from the longest visible light wavelengths (about 780 nanometers, nm) through the shortest visible light wavelength (about 380 nm). It even measures some invisible (to you) light in the ultraviolet (below about 380 nm). This instrument, called a spectrophotometer, will be set up and operated by your laboratory instructor. You are responsible for giving your sunglasses to your lab instructor and getting back a copy of the spectral "through-put", the spectrum of your sunglasses. You are also responsible for getting a copy of the spectrum of a pair of ordinary plastic lab glasses. This spectrum may be run during the experiment or may be run prior to the lab, copied, and handed out during the lab period.

After you obtain a copy of the data for your sunglasses and the plastic lab glasses, label the axes of both of the plots: the X axis is wavelength measured in nm and the Y axis is transmission. Ask your lab instructor if you are not sure about the axes labels.

Report Sheet—Experiment 19
Sunglasses, Ultraviolet Radiation, and You

Date _____   Section number _____   Name _____

1. Data

    a) Staple or paper clip the spectrum of your sunglasses to the back of this report sheet.

    b) Staple or paper clip the spectrum of the plastic lab glasses to the back of this report sheet.

2. Light transmission

    a) What percentage of the visible light gets through the lab glasses? _____ %.

    b) What percentage of ultraviolet light get through the lab glasses? _____ %.

    c) What percentage of the visible light gets through your sunglasses? _____ %.

    d) What percentage of ultraviolet light gets through your sunglasses? _____ %.

    e) Which pair of glasses does a better job of blocking UV?

3. Colored sunglasses transmission characteristics (complete only if your sunglasses have an obviously tinted lenses)

    a) How are the colors *that you can see* through you sunglasses' lenses related to their spectrum? (Describe the shape of the spectrum's curve or line.)

    b) How are the totally colorless lenses of the plastic lab glasses related to *their* spectrum?

Questions—Experiment 19
Sunglasses, Ultraviolet Radiation, and You

Date _____   Section number _____   Name _____

1. Where *does* the ultraviolet light that hits the earth come from? Are there any other extraterrestrial sources?

2. What molecule or what cycle involving this molecule in the stratosphere removes a large amount of the incoming ultraviolet radiation?

3. What percentage of the ultraviolet light shining on your particular pair sunglasses *is blocked by them*?

4. What percentage of ultraviolet light shining on a pair of ordinary plastic lab glasses *is blocked by them*?

5. Did the cost of a pair of sunglasses seem to affect their ability to block ultraviolet light? Can you think of a reason that this would be so? What is the reason?

Think, Speculate, Reflect, and Ponder

6. If a result of the Chapman Cycle is that the energy of incoming ultraviolet radiation gets converted into infrared radiation in the upper stratosphere, what happens to the temperature of the upper stratosphere because of this process? (Hint: What is the relationship between infrared energy and heat?)

7. What will the visible light transmission spectrum of a red-tinted pair of sunglasses look like? Draw this spectrum.

Experiment
20

The Apparent
Molecular Weight
of Air

Sample From Home

No samples from home are required for this experiment.

Objectives

The objective of this experiment is to allow you to measure the molecular weight of air by treating this complex mixture of a number of gases as if it were a pure gas. You will use an elegant and simple procedure that capitalizes on the sensitive ability of a three- or four-place balance to detect small changes in mass.

Background

The densities of the solids and liquids that you examined in Experiment 2, *Going Metric With the Rest of the World* are not strongly affected by changes in the physical conditions of the surroundings. The metal bar that you measured the density of in that experiment does not significantly vary with temperature unless you heat it to high temperatures and melt it!

The situation for gases is significantly different: The density of a gas depends strongly on its temperature and pressure. A mathematical equation that describes this relationship is

$$d = \frac{PM}{RT}$$

Where d = density of a gas; P = pressure; M = molecular weight; R is the gas constant; and T is Kelvin temperature.

Since the molecular weight, M, of a particular gas and the gas constant, R, are constants, the density of that gas is proportional to pressure and inversely proportional to temperature. This is a situation quite different from the effects of temperature and pressure on solids and liquids.

This result has profound effects on our weather. The positions of high and low pressure centers cause dramatic air movements because of the differences in air density. We all know that hot air rises; hot air balloons operate on this principle. This is also the reason for rapid mixing in the troposphere, the layer of the atmosphere closest to the earth. Air heated at the surface of the earth is mixed with other air masses as it rises to higher altitudes. This mixing, in effect, cleans the air by diluting (with clean air from other parts of the troposphere) the pollutants that were injected into the air at the earth's surface. During smog alerts there is often an absence of air movement due to an inversion layer. This occurs when warm air lies above cold air, thereby trapping the cold and increasingly polluted air next to the surface of the earth. Due to density effects (colder, denser air stays low and warmer, less dense air stays high) very little air movement and mixing occurs.

The effects of inversion layers upon tropospheric air quality became clear in the Los Angeles basin as early as the 1940s. Programs to clean up the air in the region were started then. Unfortunately population growth, more automobiles, and more industry have continued to outpace the remedial actions. A similar situation now exists in the Denver metropolitan area where an ugly "brown cloud" is highly visible on days when a temperature inversion is present. From the front steps of the National Center for Atmospheric Research, on a mesa above Boulder, Colorado, a layer of extremely dark polluted air can be seen often during the mid to late winter months as polluted urban air from Boulder and Denver mix together to obscure that beautiful mountain setting.

The very slow rate of vertical mixing in the stratosphere (the layer of the atmosphere above the troposphere) is caused by a natural temperature inversion. As air rises in the atmosphere it expands and cools. As a result, in the lower atmosphere, temperature tends to decrease with increasing altitude. When one reaches the stratosphere, however, this trend is reversed because of the presence of ozone. Ozone molecules absorb visible and ultraviolet radiation from the sun. This absorption of radiation heats the upper stratosphere so that the upper layers become hotter than the lower layers. The stratosphere, therefore, get warmer as altitude increases, just the opposite of the troposphere.

The cold air near the bottom of the stratosphere is relatively dense so it has little tendency to rise. The warmer air near the top of the stratosphere is less dense and has little tendency to sink. The result is that once pollutants enter the stratosphere, they tend to remain there for a very long time. The residence time (the average time present) of a pollutant in the stratosphere is known from tests of nuclear weapons in the atmosphere (before the nuclear test ban treaty of 1964; see Experiment 4, *Radioactivity*). It was found that the residence time of radioactive debris in the atmosphere ranged from about six months when injected low in the stratosphere (near 12 km) to about five years when injected high in the stratosphere (near 45 km).

The molecular weight of a compound is dependent on the atoms that make up each molecule of that compound. This means that a mole of a particular compound that contains only one kind of molecule has a well defined mass because only those kinds of molecules are present. However, for a mixture of compounds, the total mass of these molecules is made up of contributions from the masses of each of the individual molecules that are present. Just like the apparent (average) molecular weight of the elements reported on the Periodic Table is made up of contributions from the masses of the individual isotopes that are present. This experiment is entitled the Apparent Molecular Weight of Air because *air is not a pure compound containing only one kind of molecule*. In fact air contains many different molecules; however, it is mostly made up of nitrogen, oxygen, argon, and carbon dioxide. All of these molecules together contribute to the mass of a particular sample of air. If we know the volume of this sample and perform some tricky yet relatively simple manipulations of the temperature of this sample, we can derive the apparent molecular weight of the sample. For a pure gas sample (containing only one kind of molecule, like methane or carbon dioxide), this experiment would yield the molecular weight of that pure compound.

In this experiment you will make a number of observations of the mass and volume of a gas sample at two different temperatures. Be as careful as possible in measuring the mass and volume during the experiment. The sealing off of the gas sample in an Erlenmeyer flask at one point in the procedure requires the use of a tubing clamp to pinch the rubber tubing closed. Make sure that this clamp is tightly clamped at the proper place on the tubing. This is the most crucial step in the whole procedure. Ask for help with the balance if you have not been instructed in its use. You will perform this experiment in duplicate and average your results together.

An example calculation is included after the report sheet to help you perform the calculations for your experimental data correctly. This example data computes the molecular weight of gas from a Bunsen burner.

Procedure

1. Set up the apparatus as demonstrated by your lab instructor and as diagrammed in Figure 20.1. Use a small amount of glycerine to aid in the insertion of the small piece of glass tubing into the one-hole stopper (# 6). Insert a 3 inch piece of glass tubing (1/8 inch inside diameter) into a one-hole stopper. Make sure that the glass tubing does not extend below the bottom of the stopper. Put a 2 1/2 inch piece of rubber tubing on the end of the glass tubing that sticks out of the top of the rubber stopper. Make sure that the rubber tubing diameter is small enough that it makes a tight seal to the glass. Place a tubing pinch clamp (or screw clamp) snugly *about the glass tubing* so that air can easily escape from the flask as you heat up the apparatus in **Step 5**. Do not clamp the rubber tubing at this time. Put the stopper *snugly* into the mouth of a 250 mL Erlenmeyer flask.

2. Weigh the entire apparatus (250 mL flask, stopper, tubing, and clamp) and record the weight to 0.001 g. Clamp a large iron ring to a ring stand. Put a piece of wire gauze with a ceramic center on the iron ring. Place an 800 or 1000 mL beaker on the gauze and clamp it to the ring stand if a beaker clamp is available.

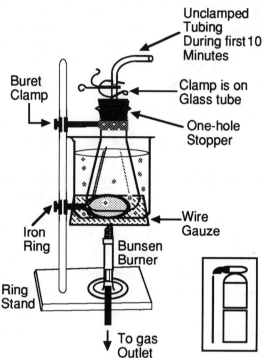

Figure 20.1. *Apparatus during first ten minutes of boiling with rubber tubing <u>unclamped</u>.*

3. Using a large buret clamp, clamp the neck of the Erlenmeyer flask so that it is down inside the beaker as much as possible.

4. Fill the beaker (containing the clamped Erlenmeyer) with water almost to the beaker's lip, allowing only enough room (about 1/2 inch) for bubbling due to rapid boiling when you heat the water.

5. Record the temperature of the water to 1 ° C. Light a Bunsen burner with a match; adjust the flame to a clean, hot, blue flame (see Experiment 1, *The Ubiquitous Bunsen Burner*). Heat the water to a boil. Boil for 10 minutes.

6. After 10 minutes of boiling, record the temperature of the water to 1° *without allowing the tip of the thermometer to touch any of the glass (either the edge of the beaker or the Erlenmeyer).*

7. With the water still boiling, use the pinch clamp to close the rubber tubing tightly. Make sure that the clamp is firmly closing off the rubber tubing's entire diameter.

8. Carefully raise the closed Erlenmeyer system out of the boiling water. Leave the beaker stationary on the wire gauze.

9. Place the Erlenmeyer flask, still tightly clamped, on a folded paper towel and dry it thoroughly with a second paper towel or Kimwipe. *Do not remove the clamp.*

10. After the Erlenmeyer cools to room temperature, weigh it to 0.001 g *while the rubber tubing is still tightly clamped.*

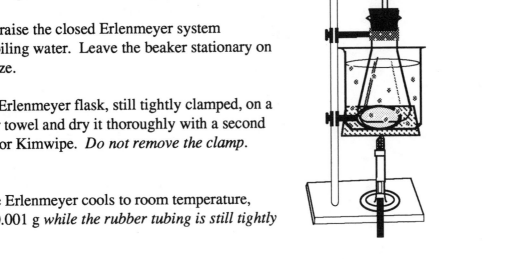

Figure 20.2. *Apparatus just before removal from boiling water with rubber tubing* clamped.

After you get the weight of the closed, room temperature system, you can test to see if you were successful in your attempts to clamp off the system and trap the air inside. After you have recorded on the report sheet the mass of the clamped Erlenmeyer, listen carefully as you unclamp the rubber tubing. If you were successful you will hear a satisfying hiss as air rushes into the flask. If you do not hear a hiss then you might have had a leaky experimental apparatus (clamped tubing or rubber stopper), and you should repeat this particular trial.

11. In order to determine the volume of the flask apparatus, remove the stopper from the mouth of the Erlenmeyer and fill the flask with water.

12. Push the stopper back into the flask, forcing water to fill the glass and rubber tubing. With the stopper still in place, dry off any excess water.

13. Pour *all* of the water from this system into a 500 mL graduated cylinder and record the volume of the apparatus (in liters) in the data table on the report sheet.

14. Repeat the entire procedure from **Step 1**. Make sure that you start your second trial with a room temperature apparatus when you are doing the first weighing.

15. Get the atmospheric pressure in the laboratory from the lab instructor who should report this value to you in atmospheres. The temperature readings that you record on the data sheet in degrees Celsius must be converted to Kelvin for the calculations. This is easily accomplished by adding 273 to all of your Celsius readings. Record these Kelvin temperatures in the data table in the appropriate place. Look at the sample calculation performed on the page after your report sheet for help with your calculations.

Report Sheet—Experiment 20
The Apparent Molecular Weight of Air

Date _____   Section number _____   Name _____

1. Data table

	Trial # 1	Trial # 2
Initial Mass of Apparatus	g	g
Final Mass of Apparatus	g	g
Change in Mass	g	g
Final Temperature of Water, T_2	°C / K	°C / K
Initial Temperature of Water, T_1	°C / K	°C / K
Change in Temperature	°	°
Volume of Apparatus (air)	L	L
Atmospheric Pressure Today	atm	atm

2. Calculations (all calculations involving temperatures use Kelvin)—See example next page.

	Trial # 1	Trial # 2

a) Calculate the mass of air in the system (at T_1)
(**use Kelvin Temperature**!)
(multiply the change in mass times T_2
then divide the result by (T_2 minus T_1)) =   _____ g   _____ g.

b) Calculate the density of the air (at T_1)
(divide the mass of air, 2(a) by
the volume of air from the data table) =   _____ g/L   _____ g/L.

c) Atmospheric pressure in the laboratory
(in atmospheres from data table)   _____ atm.

d) Temperature in laboratory (Kelvin)   _____ K.

e) Calculate the apparent molecular weight of air
(multiply the density of air 2(b) by 0.08206;
multiply this result by the lab temperature 2(d);
divide the result by the air pressure in the lab 2(c) =   ___ g/mole   ___ g/mole.

e) Average of your two apparent molecular weights   _____ g/mole.

Example Calculation
Bunsen Burner Gas

1. Example data table

	Trial # 1	Trial # 2
Initial Mass of Apparatus	148.551 g	g
Final Mass of Apparatus	148.516 g	g
Change in Mass	0.035 g	g
Final Temperature of Water, T_2	100 °C 373 K	°C K
Initial Temperature of Water, T_1	25 °C 298 K	°C K
Change in Temperature	75 °	°
Volume of Apparatus (air)	0.265 L	L
Atmospheric Pressure Today	1.010 atm	atm

2. Example calculations (all calculations involving temperatures use Kelvin)

a) Calculate the mass of air in the system (at T_1)
(**use Kelvin Temperature!**)
(multiply the change in mass times T_2
then divide the result by (T_2 minus T_1)) =

Example Trial

$$\frac{0.035 \times 373}{75}$$

0.174 g.

b) Calculate the density of the air (at T_1)
(divide the mass of air, 2(a) by
the volume of air from the data table) =

$$\frac{0.174}{0.265}$$

0.657 g/L.

c) Atmospheric pressure in the laboratory
(in atmospheres)

1.010 atm.

d) Temperature in laboratory (Kelvin)

298 K.

e) Calculate the apparent molecular weight of air
(multiply the density of air 2(b) by the gas constant
0.08206; multiply this result by the temperature
in the lab 2(d) in Kelvin and divide the
result by the air pressure in the lab 2(c) =.

$$\frac{0.657 \times 0.08206 \times 298}{1.010}$$

15.9 g/mole.

Questions—Experiment 20
The Apparent Molecular Weight of Air

Date _____   Section number _____   Name _____

1. Would this experimental procedure work for the calculation of the molecular weight of a pure gas?

2. How could you modify the procedure to accomplish this?

3. If you performed this procedure on the top of Mount Everest, would the apparent molecular weight of air that you determined be the same as if you performed this procedure at sea level? (Hint: Reread the background in this experiment and Experiment 5, O_2 *Content of Air*.)

Think, Speculate, Reflect, and Ponder

4. Why is the temperature of boiling water not 100 ° C at altitudes substantially higher than sea level? (An error in thermometer calibration is not the answer.)

5. Why might the word boiling occur to astronauts just after their space suits rupture in space during a space walk?

The World of Plastics and Synthetics

The next three experiments illustrate the preparation of some commonly encountered giant molecules using the chemical process of polymerization. Some properties of these polymers will be examined, and you can use one of them for embedding a sample from home.

Background

We should begin by answering the question, "Just what is a polymer?" A chemist might say that "A polymer is a molecule made out of monomers." But what, then, is a monomer, and how does it differ from any ordinary molecule?

Most molecules can be characterized as having a particular reactive site (chemists would say "functional groups") which, as the name implies, can react — combine with — reactive sites in other molecules to form a single bigger molecule. In very general terms, we could diagram this concept as follows where the "hooks" represent potential chemical bonds due to these reactive sites.

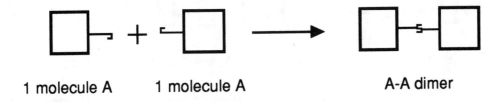

1 molecule A   1 molecule A   A-A dimer

The single molecules are monomers (mono = one) and the larger molecule would be called a dimer (di = two). But once we make the dimer, we cannot go any further since there are no more reactive sites available for joining together with still more molecules.

But what if one of the molecules had the potential to form not one but two chemical "hooks" per molecule? Then we could write:

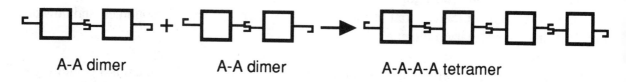

1 molecule A   2 molecules B   B-A-B trimer

Now we have made a trimer (tri = three) by joining together a total of three monomer molecules, but here again the reaction must stop at this point since no more chemical hooks are left in the trimer.

You should now be able to guess the last chapter in this polymer story — how can molecules be designed so that they can continue to combine with each other almost indefinitely to produce a polymer? In order for this to happen, all of the monomer molecules must have the potential to form chemical bonds in both directions, i.e., have, in effect, two chemical hooks. Let's diagram what can happen in such a case:

monomer A   monomer A   A-A dimer

But the initial dimer itself still has two available hooks at each end, so ...

A-A dimer   A-A dimer   A-A-A-A tetramer

Now the tetramer (tetra = 4) itself has still two hooks on each end which enable it to continue combining with more molecules in both directions with either more monomer, or maybe another tetramer forming an octamer:

2 A-A-A-A tetramers   A-A-A-A-A-A-A-A octamer

So where do we stop? Not until we use up all the reactants or "hooks" (monomer starting material), at which point we have a truly giant "mer" called a polymer. Monomers are thus simply molecules which may be identical or different, but all have the ability to form bonds in at least two directions, while polymers (poly = many) simply consist of usually thousands of monomer units all chemically joined together in one giant molecule. Whereas most ordinary molecules have molecular weights not greater than a few hundred, polymers typically have molecular weights from tens of thousands to many millions. Some of these large polymers are even big enough to see with special instruments like the electron microscope, although the individual atoms themselves still cannot be discerned. Most polymerizations also require small amounts of chemical reaction initiators (catalysts) to cause the monomer molecules to react at a practical rate.

But do not be too quick to give human beings credit for inventing polymers, for they were present long before humans even made the earth scene. For example, the fibrous part of plants is principally cellulose, a polymer of glucose that gives bulk to our diet but is indigestible in humans and thus provides us with no food value.

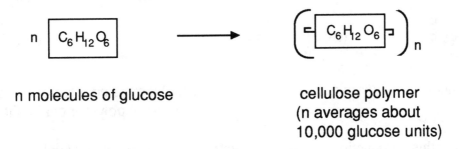

n molecules of glucose

cellulose polymer
(n averages about
10,000 glucose units)

Starch too is a polymer—and also a polymer of glucose. We can, however, digest starch and obtain food value from it. If that sounds impossible or intriguing, perhaps you will decide to study organic chemistry in three dimensions to find out the answer.

There exist, in fact, an almost endless variety of natural polymers which are found in nature—biopolymers each having its own special and indispensable function in a particular living system, such as proteins and many carbohydrates. Scientists's initial efforts were thus directed at discovering, understanding and duplicating these biopolymers and improving upon them or synthesizing new ones designed to suit their own needs.

Rubber, for example, is formed by the coagulation of the juice (latex) of trees or shrubs that are successfully grown in the Far East, South America, and Africa. As is so often the case, real progress results only when a necessary determination is added to resourcefulness. Thus when World War II drastically and dangerously cut into the supply of rubber to the United States, determination coupled with necessary financing resulted in the production of a number of rubber-like substances, some of which were equal or superior to natural rubber for tires and other special uses. The development of these various synthetic polymers indicated that it is not necessary to duplicate or even approximate the chemical structure of natural rubber to produce an elastic plastic.

Almost all articles commonly referred to as a "synthetic" or "plastic" represent a polymer made by humans. Since most of these polymers come ultimately from petroleum, we can better appreciate the need to conserve our remaining petroleum resources for these purposes rather than burning them up as fuel. Alternate energy sources can be developed, but once the world's petroleum resources are gone, so will be the raw materials to make much or most of what we wear, build with, ride in, drink from, sit in, cook with, and otherwise depend on for our supposed "good" life. The development of the whole field of polymer chemistry has given us a wide variety of elastic and nonelastic materials which the consumer today takes for granted.

Two of the more common synthetic condensation polymers appear below. Both of these reactions split out a water molecule as one of the products in addition to the copolymer product.

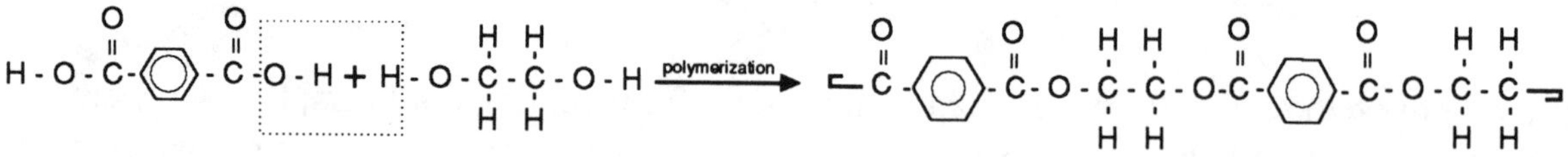

tetraphthalic acid   ethylene glycol

a polyester copolymer (Dacron)
(part of polymer chain shown)

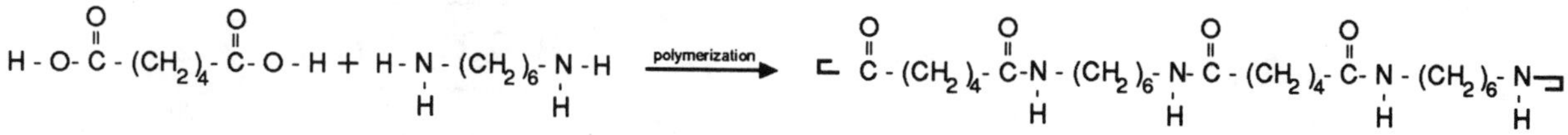

adipic acid   1,6 diaminohexane

a polyamide copolymer (Nylon 6,6)
(part of polymer chain shown)

We round out this introduction to polymers with four very common vinyl polymers: polyethylene (used in plastic bags and film), polyvinyl chloride (used in floor tiles, plastic plumbing pipes, and garden hoses), polystyrene (used in "styrofoam" cups, food packaging, insulation, and plastic furniture), and Teflon ® (used for cooking utensil coatings, superslide bearings, and electrical insulation):

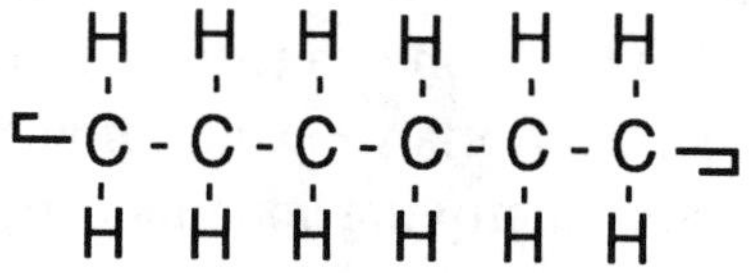

polyethylene

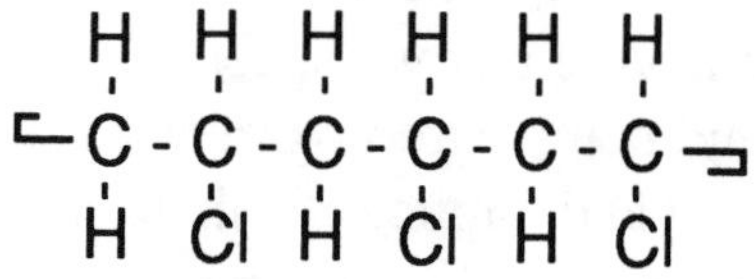

polyvinyl chloride

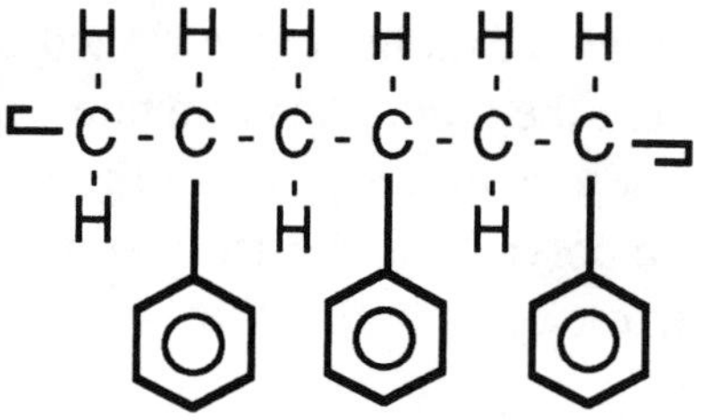

polystyrene

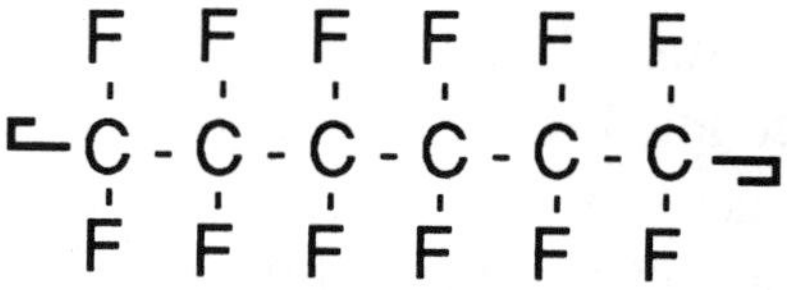

Teflon

Experiment
21

Polyamide: Nylon

Sample From Home

No samples from home are needed for this experiment.

Objectives

You will mix two monomers together and produce a nylon polymer which can be drawn out into a pliable rope. You can then measure the overall length of the Nylon "rope" you have made from one fourth cup of liquid.

$$n \begin{array}{c} O \\ \parallel \\ Cl\text{-}C \end{array}\text{-}(CH_2)_8 \begin{array}{c} O \\ \parallel \\ C\text{-}Cl \end{array} + n\ H_2N\text{-}(CH_2)_6\text{-}NH_2 \longrightarrow \left(\begin{array}{c} O \\ \parallel \\ C \end{array}\text{-}(CH_2)_8 \begin{array}{c} O \\ \parallel \\ C \end{array}\text{-} \begin{array}{c} H \\ \cdot \\ N \end{array}\text{-}(CH_2)_6\text{-} \begin{array}{c} H \\ \cdot \\ N \end{array} \right)_n + n\ HCl$$

sebacoyl chloride   1,6–hexanediamine   a nylon polymer   hydrogen chloride

Background

One common way to join molecular units together to produce giant molecules is called condensation polymerization, where a small molecule like H_2O or HCl is "split out" and eliminated during the reaction. A classic example of this is one for which the DuPont Company spent hundreds of thousands of dollars in the early pioneering days at the dawn of polymer research in the hope that something practical and monetarily useful to the Company might be forthcoming. After initial discovery, millions of dollars had to go into the development of suitable manufacturing processes before the new polymer could be consumer produced. In the case of nylon, DuPont's gamble paid off.

In practice, nylon fiber is actually spun from a melt and pulled to give it desirable tensile strength. Although there are different nylon type polymers (depending upon the specific monomers used), the reaction in this experiment is illustrative. Nylon is thus a copolymer made by the chemical combination of two different monomers. The boxed groups of atoms at each end of the two monomer molecules represent the two reactive sites - our chemical hooks. Molecular weights of the polymer molecules can be expected to average around 15,000 where n = 52 units.

Each of the reactants is dissolved separately in two liquids that do not dissolve in each other (water and tetrachloroethylene). When these two solutions are brought together the monomers can react with each other only where the two liquids are in contact — called the interface. It is from this polymer film that forms at the interface between these liquids that the nylon rope is drawn. As soon as old polymer film is removed, new film immediately forms and so the reaction results in the continuous creation of more and more polymer until all the reactant monomers are consumed.

Procedure

CAUTION: Do not breathe vapors nor let any of the chemicals in this experiment contact your skin; the diamine is especially toxic. If an accident occurs, wash the contaminated area with soap and water immediately and notify your lab instructor. Good ventilation is necessary in the laboratory for this experiment: Make sure that the ventilation hoods are working well before you start this experiment.

Use your engineering aptitude and position necessary beakers and glass rods as diagrammed in Figure 21.1. The rods can best be mounted by inserting one end of each into a cork or stopper and gripping with a burette clamp attached to a separate ring stand. The 600 mL collection beaker is filled about 2/3 full with water and placed onto the floor. To get the desired height of fall, you will probably also have to raise the height of the beaker in which the polymer is made about a foot above the bench top with blocks or other suitable props.

USE DISPOSABLE PLASTIC GLOVES WHILE DOING PROCEDURE STEP 1.

1. The nylon rope monomer solutions have already been made for you. Pour 50 mL of the sebacoyl chloride/tetrachloroethylene solution into a 100 mL beaker. Very carefully and slowly layer 25 mL of the 1,6 hexanediamine/water solution on top of the tetrachloroethylene so that a MINIMUM OF MIXING of the two layers results. <u>Do not stir</u>. It may help to pour the water solution down a funnel with the tip held against side of beaker just above surface of the tetra-chloroethylene layer.

      (a) Note observations on the report sheet.

You can try dyeing your polymer by adding safranin 0 (glow-red) or orcein (purple) to the 100 mL reaction beaker. Only a B–B sized pinch dropped in the top liquid layer is needed.

Reach down through the top (aqueous) liquid layer and grasp the center of the interfacial polymer film with tweezers and slowly pull the mass up through the water layer. Bring the nylon "rope" up from the center of the beaker, over both the glass rods and then allow it to fall into the beaker. With a little experimenting with the distance between the glass rods, rod angles, and teamwork the height of the nylon rope falling over the glass rod can be adjusted so that this weight of rope will be sufficient to keep automatically pulling more rope from the solution. Avoid touching the nylon rope as much as possible to prevent the reagents from unnecessarily contact-ing your gloves. If you do get the chemicals on your hands, wash up with soap and water and contact the lab instructor. You can perhaps try winding the rope up on the outside of a large beaker to avoid tangling as it forms.

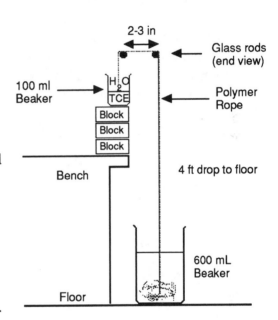

Figure 21.1. *Nylon rope "in production."*

When the polymerization is finished, wash the polymer rope in your 600 mL collection beaker in running cold water for a couple of minutes. Drain off all of the water, add a mixture of 25 mL water plus 25 mL of acetone and agitate gently to wash the polymer thoroughly with this solvent. Pour off the acetone/water solution into an appropriate waste container, refill the beaker with water and gently lift out your nylon "rope" and stretch it out on the bench top. Pour the tetra-chloroethylene layer remaining in your 100 mL reaction beaker into the appropriate lab container labeled for that purpose.

It takes a lot of care, patience, technique (& luck!) to be able to untangle your rope. After wash-ing with water and while the rope is still in the 600 mL beaker, try sticking one end of the rope onto the table top. Then walk along with the beaker and simultaneously pull the rope out and onto top of bench with your hand. If your rope just won't untangle in a reasonable length of time (20 minutes), cut it into pieces sufficient so you can at least estimate its length. One hundred feet is an excellent "score".

2. Perform the following tests on the nylon rope:

(a) Describe the color, appearance, texture, shape and tensile strength of your damp nylon rope.

(b) Spread out your polymer on the desk top in such a way that you can measure its total length with a meter stick. Record your results.

(c) Test the inertness (nonreactivity) of your polymer towards the solvent acetone by placing a pea-sized polymer wad into about 10 mL of acetone in a 50 mL beaker. *CAUTION: Acetone is flammable. Extinguish any flames near work area.* If the nylon becomes sticky, this indicates that it is being dissolved by this solvent.

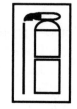

Note observations and dispose of the liquid and the polymer wad in a suitable waste receptacle. If you wish, your remaining rope may be rolled up around something suitable and taken home. (The Nylon will, however, become very brittle when dry since no "plasticizer" chemical was added to keep the rope flexible.)

Report Sheet—Experiment 21
Polyamide: Nylon

Date _____   **Section number** _____   **Name** _____

1. (a) Observations when sebacoyl chloride and 1, 6-hexanediamine solutions contact.

2. (a) Physical properties of nylon rope:

    Color_____.

    Texture_____.

    Shape_____.

    Tensile strength_____.

    (b) Total length of rope from 40 mL of solution.
        (Stretch it out around lab!)

        _____ meters.

        _____ feet.

    (c) Solvent resistance of polymer towards acetone_____

    _____.

3. Comments and conclusions on experiment

Questions—Experiment 21
Polyamide: Nylon

Date _____   Section number _____   Name _____

1. What do you think might be the purpose of washing the newly formed polymer with an acetone/water solution?

2. List three principle consumer uses for nylon.

(a)

(b)

(c)

Think, Speculate, Reflect, and Ponder

3. Household utensils made of plastic are now a commonplace item. Mention some household items that have not been successfully fabricated from plastic. Do you expect that any of these articles you have mentioned can or will be made out of plastic in the future? Why or why not?

4. Regarding polymers, why doesn't it make sense to burn up all the petroleum reserves for energy before switching to alternate energy sources?

Experiment

22

Polystyrene

Sample From Home

If you choose, you may bring any small object (picture, ring, agate, coin, etc.) that you would like to embed in plastic.

Objectives

Continuing our investigation of polymers, you will make polystyrene, an addition polymer, and you have the option of embedding an object of your choice in this piece of solid, clear plastic.

Background

Along with polyethylene (Tupperware, plastic tarpaulins, etc.), polystyrene is one of the most widespread of all man–made plastics, due in large part to the fact that both of these polymers are relatively cheap to produce. Polystyrene can be molded into solid shapes as well as foamed. Such molded polystyrene objects might also be termed "cheap" in another sense due to the ease with which they crack and break. Its cheapness however, makes it economical even as a paper substitute for some applications where both food (e.g., meats at the supermarket) and breakable objects are packed using foamed polystyrene.

However, an increasing number of such foamed products ("Styrofoam") are being banned by states since the low boiling liquid methylene chloride often used as the foaming agent is thought to be harmful to the earth's ozone layer. The ozone layer is a chemical shield in the stratosphere that protects the surface of the earth from harmful ultraviolet radiation from the sun. McDonald's has now banned styrofoam packaging from their Big Mac family of fast foods.

Unlike nylon, polystyrene (as well as polyurethane in the next experiment) is produced simply by the joining together of monomer molecules without "splitting out" any small molecules in the process. This process is called addition polymerization:

$$n \quad \underset{\underset{\bigcirc}{\overset{H}{|}}}{C} = CH_2 \quad \xrightarrow[\text{Catalyst}]{\text{Peroxide}} \quad \left[\underset{\underset{H}{\overset{H}{|}}{\underset{\bigcirc}{\overset{|}{C}}}}{\overset{H}{\underset{|}{C}}} - \underset{\underset{H}{\overset{H}{|}}}{\overset{H}{\underset{|}{C}}} \right]_n$$

Styrene (monomer)   Polystyrene chain

Each hexagon in these structures represents a ring of six carbon atoms. Molecular weights of the polymer molecules may average up to 500,000.

The 2-butanone peroxide serves as the catalyst to initiate the polymerization so that it will proceed fast enough to be complete before the end of the lab period. Because timing is critical, you must pay close attention to the mixing and setting times for this reaction as mentioned in the procedure.

Procedure

Good ventilation is necessary for this experimental procedure, and you will need to mix and react the monomer in a hood. Because of the clean-up difficulties, we will avoid getting the monomer mix solutions on the lab glassware. Determine a 20 mL volume in the waxed paper cup provided by pouring 20 mL of water into one cup and marking the water level on the outside with a pen or pencil. (This process is called "calibrating" your cup). Use this mark to calibrate two empty dry cups at the 20 mL volume level, and then either discard your cup plus water or let someone else use it for their calibration.

CAUTION: *USE DISPOSABLE GLOVES WHEN HANDLING STYRENE MONOMER IN **PARTS 1** AND **2**.*

1. Fill just one of your calibrated cups to the 20 mL mark with styrene resin and add approximately 8 drops of the peroxide catalyst.

TAKE CARE THAT ABSOLUTELY NO TRACE OF CONTAMINATION BETWEEN THE STYRENE AND PEROXIDE STOCK CONTAINERS OCCURS WHEN YOU GET YOUR SAMPLE. Mix thoroughly by swirling the cup contents for 2 minutes.

If you choose to stir, do so slowly to minimize incorporating air bubbles into your liquid. If you wish to try giving a colored tint to this one half of your plastic block, add a BB sized pinch of Sudan III or IV red dye to your monomer solution at this point. (The names of these dyes should be color explanatory if not chemically meaningful.) When you brew up the second batch of monomer in **Part 2**, you can elect whether to add color to it or just leave it clear.

A typical gel time is 10 minutes @ 22 ° C.

> **(a)** Note the room (catalyst) temperature and time of catalyst addition and record the total minutes elapsed before gelling begins.

> **(b)** Note the characteristics of the monomer solution at this point (viscosity, color, odor).

Select some object of your choice to embed if you wish, such as a picture, ring, agate, coin, etc. Leaves and flowers can be preserved, but they must be specially treated first to remove water and air from the tissue in order to obtain a perfectly clear block.

2. About five minutes after you mix the first monomer batch, mix a second batch of styrene monomer plus catalyst in your second calibrated paper cup (color may be added as before, if desired). Drop your object to be embedded into this second batch. When the first batch has gelled enough to support the object you plan to embed, remove the object from the second batch with tweezers and place it on top of the first batch in the position you want, top down. Then pour the second batch of resin on top of the first. Remove any air bubbles with the aid of a toothpick or wire. The second batch of resin should become sufficiently hard in 30–45 minutes after initial mixing to remove the whole plastic block from the cup.

NOTE: Resin cup should be warm to the touch during hardening. If it gets too hot to touch comfortably, place the lower 1/2 of the cup into some cold water for a few minutes; otherwise, excessive heat will cause cracks in your casting. Or if resin is not hardening quickly enough, try putting the lower 1/2 of the cup into some hot water.

Describe your observations. (You can polish the flat surfaces of your casting later by rubbing it over a piece of very fine emery paper moistened with water).

3. Although most of the curing/hardening process is not complete for several hours (actually, it never completely stops), we can still proceed with the following tests forthwith:

(a) Describe the hardness, texture, color, and general appearance of your plastic casting.

(b) Test the inertness of your polystyrene plastic casting towards the solvent acetone (nail polish remover) by letting a few drops of acetone fall onto a surface of your casting. CAUTION: *Acetone is flammable. Make sure that no flames are near the work area.* Rub the surface with your finger where the acetone has been dropped. If the surface becomes sticky, this indicates that it is being dissolved by this solvent.

Note your observations on the report sheet.

(c) Weigh your cast plastic object and then determine its volume using the methods described in Experiment 2, *Going Metric with the Rest of the World.* You will have to obtain a graduated cylinder just large enough for your object to slip into (probably a 1000 mL size). Use these data to calculate the density of your casting.

Report Sheet—Experiment 22
Polystyrene

Date _____   **Section number** _____   **Name** _____

1. Monomer/catalyst mixture
   Room temperature   _____° C.

   (a) Time required for gel   _____ min.

   (b) Physical properties

       Viscosity_____.

       Color _____.

       Odor _____.

2. General observations during preparation of plastic block

3. Polystyrene plastic

   (a) Physical properties

       Hardness _____.

       Texture _____.

       Color _____.

   (b) Solvent resistance of polystyrene plastic towards acetone _____.

   (c) Density of polystyrene block

       Weight of block (to nearest 0.1g)   _____ g.

       Volume of block (to nearest 1 mL)   _____ mL =   _____ cm³.

       Calculated density
       (divide the mass by the volume) =   _____ g/cm³.

4. Comments and conclusions on the experiment

Date _____   Section number _____   Name _____

1. You were cautioned not to permit the slightest contamination between the styrene and peroxide stock containers. What might happen if these precautions were ignored?

2. Would your plastic block float or sink if dropped into the great Salt Lake in Utah? (Density = 1.1 g/cm³) (Show calculations for your sample to back up your answer.)

3. Why does the price of oil affect the price of plastics?

4. In general terms, how do you think this procedure would have to be changed in order to make a foamed instead of solid cast block of polystyrene? (Hint: What is the difference between leavened and unleavened bread? Also, see this experiment's introduction.)

Think, Speculate, Reflect, and Ponder

5. Why were only very small amounts of 2-butanone required in this experiment? (Hint: Look up the term catalyst.)

6. Would the procedure's methods describing ways to change the temperature of the polymerization reaction vessel (the paper cup) also change the rate of the ongoing reaction? Explain.

Experiment
23

Polyurethane

Sample From Home

No samples from home are needed for this experiment.

Objectives

In completing our study of polymerization, we will investigate another type of addition polymerization reaction. However, instead of obtaining a solid block of plastic, a rigid foam will be produced.

Background

Although more expensive than polystyrene plastics, polyurethanes have found extensive application in home and industry. Not only are the foams relatively inert, but they also have good insulating properties which makes them attractive for use in refrigerator and freezer walls. And because of the extreme lightness and rigidity which can be given to the foam, lamination of this foam into hollow structural components can produce very strong, rigid, but light panels especially valuable to the aircraft industry.

Polyurethane formulations can furthermore be altered to give a nonrigid elastic foam, such as that commonly found in pillows and cushions. "Spandex" elastic fibers are a urethane type polymer. Other modifications can yield very durable imitation leather products ("Corfam") which have the ability to "breathe" air and water vapor through its pores like real leather. This is especially important in shoes. These are only a few of the many uses for this polymer, but they should be enough to indicate the importance and versatility of this synthetic "plastic."

The two viscous solutions A and B used in this experiment contain both the two monomers (the polymerization thus produces a copolymer) as well as the catalyst necessary to make the reaction proceed at a practical rate. Upon mixing, the hooking together of the monomers (the polymerization) begins. On a molecular level, this reaction is an addition polymerization like polystyrene and looks approximately like the following horrible mess when expressed in chemist's notation:

The boxed groups of atoms represent the reactive sites (our chemical hooks) which serve to join the whole polymer together, while each hexagon represents a ring of six carbon atoms. Written out in words this translates to: Toluene 2,4-diisocyanate reacts with poly (propylene oxide) glycol (this is a polymer itself) to produce polyurethane.

But if this were all that happened, you would end up with just a solid, intractable glob. With no foaming agent, it would be like trying to bake a cake without any baking powder—no rising and foaming of the product would result. So just as cakes and breads rely on a chemical reaction to produce carbon dioxide gas for foaming, so does our polyurethane reaction. Some of these N=C=O groups that you see on the toluene diisocyanate molecules react with the water present to produce the CO_2 necessary for frothing.

Although timing can be important in all chemical reactions, it is critical when carrying out polymerizations and especially so with polyurethane foam preparations. Different commercial formulations will vary somewhat in their specifications, but in general, mixing of the two solutions A and B must be completed within 30–60 seconds. After this time foaming accelerates rapidly as the mixture expands to about twenty times its original volume. Foaming requires 3–5 minutes, and most further chemical reactions are complete in 20–30 minutes. The full strength of the foam is not reached until 24 hours of cure time has passed. Just like the saying "time waits for no one," once mixed, neither do chemicals!

Procedure

CAUTION: *The isocyanate monomer used in this experiment is very toxic—both by breathing and skin contact. All polymerization work must be done in a hood using the heavy plastic bags provided for that purpose. USE DISPOSABLE PLASTIC GLOVES.*

Good ventilation is necessary in the lab for this experiment. Because of the clean–up difficulties, we will avoid getting the monomer liquids or the polymer itself on the lab glassware. Determine a 25 mL volume in two waxed paper cups provided by pouring 25 mL of water into each of them and marking the water level on the outside of each cup with a pen or pencil. (This process is called "calibrating" your cup). Discard the water and blot out residual water with a dry towel.

1. Using the plastic gloves provided, fill one of your two calibrated cups to the 25 mL mark with monomer A solution, and the other with monomer B. TAKE CARE THAT ABSOLUTELY NO TRACE OF CONTAMINATION BETWEEN A AND B CONTAINERS OCCURS WHEN YOU TAKE YOUR SAMPLES. Note visible characteristics of the monomer solutions (viscosity, color), but *do not smell the solutions*!

2. Pour the less viscous (less thick) monomer into the other, scraping out the last bit of liquid with a wooden tongue depressor. Mix well and without delay (within 30-45 seconds), drop the cup containing the monomer mix into a one quart-size plastic bag. Note your observations.

3. After your polymer foam has set, cooked, and cooled, (30-45 minutes), perform the following tests on your product:

> **(a)** Describe the porosity, rigidity (compression resistance), texture, color, and general appearance of your polyurethane foam.

> **(b)** Test the inertness of your polymer foam towards the solvent acetone (nail polish remover).

Since ACETONE is a flammable organic liquid, you must first MAKE SURE THAT NO FLAMES are near your work area before proceeding. Perform the test by placing a pea-sized piece of foam into a crucible and adding about 3 mL of acetone. If the foam collapses or becomes sticky, this indicates that it is being attacked by this solvent. Record your observations. Pour any remaining liquid directly into the sink drain and discard residual polymer into a suitable receptacle.

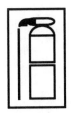

(c) Determine the approximate density of a golf ball size piece of foam by measuring its weight (first) and volume (second) using the methods previously described for density determinations in Experiment 2, *Going Metric with the Rest of the World.* You will have to obtain a graduated cylinder just large enough for your foam to slip into. Use your ingenuity to submerge the foam and get an acceptably accurate measurement of the water displacement.

Report Sheet—Experiment 23
Polyurethane Foam

Date _____   **Section number** _____   **Name** _____

1. Appearance of

    Monomer Solution A _____.

    Monomer Solution B _____.

2. Observations upon mixing

3. Polyurethane foam
    (a) Physical properties

    Porosity _____.

    Rigidity _____.

    Texture _____.

    Color _____.

    (b) Solvent resistance of foam towards

    Acetone _____.

    (c) Density of polyurethane foam

    Weight of foam piece (to nearest 0.01g)   _____ g.

    Volume of foam
    (to nearest 1 mL, or 0.1 mL if possible)   _____ mL = _____ cm^3.

    Calculated density
    (divide mass by volume) =   _____ g/cm^3.

4. Comments and conclusions on experiment

Questions—Experiment 23
Polyurethane Foam

Date _____   **Section number** _____   **Name** _____

1. Considering only buoyancy effect, would you rather have a 1000 cm³ block of polyurethane foam or a 1000 cm³ block of cork (density = 0.2g/cm³) to hold onto in order to keep from drowning? Support your choice by suitable calculations.

2. Where do we obtain the raw materials to make most plastics?

3. How was your foaming produced? What gas was used, and where did the atoms making up the gas come from? (HINT: See the background to this experiment.)

4. Consider the polymerization process itself:

(a) Directions for carrying out polymerizations usually refer to a minimum temperature for use. Why is that?

(b) What disadvantage might there be if the temperature were too hot?

Think, Speculate, Reflect, and Ponder

5. Considering all of the polymers in this and the last two experiments, describe two of the difficulties that would be encountered in designing a plastics recycling program that requires the separation of each kind of plastic before the material could be recycled.

Hangover Havens
Salicylic Acid Derivatives
(Aspirin and Oil of Wintergreen)

Sample From Home

No samples from home are needed for this experiment.

Objectives

This experiment will demonstrate a simple synthesis of two well-known medicinal compounds—aspirin and oil of wintergreen. The quantitative yield of aspirin product will be determined.

Background

lysergic acid diethylamide (LSD)

salicylic acid

The lines in the above formulae refer to chemical bonds, and each geometrical corner stands for a carbon atom unless otherwise indicated.

LSD is a dangerous drug enabling one to take a temporary but not very safe trip from reality. Its hallucinogenic effects were accidently discovered in 1943 and can be produced by an oral dose as small as 50 micrograms (0.00005 g). Salicylic acid, on the other hand, was first prepared back in 1838, and by the late 1800s doses of 0.5 g or more were found to offer not an escape from reality, but a relatively safe temporary escape from headaches brought on by worldly tensions. In addition to its pain reducing (analgesic) effects, salicylic acid combats fever (antipyretic), relieves arthritic pains (anti-inflammatory), and has a low toxicity with no LSD type flashbacks. It thus assumes considerable importance indeed as a drug to relieve the symptoms of several of human beings' most common ailments.

Its beneficial effects notwithstanding, however, salicylic acid also produces a number of unpleasant side effects in many individuals. For this reason, the organic chemist sought to modify its structure slightly in a way to keep its beneficial properties while eliminating or at least reducing the undesired effects. This chemical modification is exactly what is practiced by chemists today—whether developing an optimum drug with a minimum toxicity or an optimum nerve gas of maximum toxicity. The molecular structure is altered until maximum potency is reached.

The particular chemical modification most widely utilized in the case of salicylic acid is called acetylation. This is one of the chemical changes you will carry out in this experiment.

salicylic acid | acetic anhydride (acetylating agent) | acetyl salicylic acid (aspirin) | acetic acid

As the boxes in the structures indicate, this modification results in a hydrogen atom of the hydroxyl group attached to the ring on salicylic acid being replaced by an acetyl $\left(\begin{array}{c}O\\ \parallel\\ \text{—C—CH}_3\end{array}\right)$ group.

This chemically modified salicylic acid, called acetylsalicylic acid or more commonly just aspirin or ASA, was first put onto the market in 1899. The annual production of aspirin in the United States peaked in 1980 at 34 million pounds but dropped to 24 million by 1988, a decline undoubtedly due to health safety concerns and the availability of aspirin substitutes like acetaminophen (Tylenol) and Ibuprofin.

Standard five grain tablets contain 0.324 g of aspirin, but in practice, somewhat less than half of the annual production of aspirin ends up in "pure" aspirin tablets. The rest is formulated along with other ingredients like buffers, special coatings, and caffeine into a wide variety of products heavily advertised to be "better" than aspirin alone. Thus the annual production of aspirin and aspirin containing tablets must still be more than enough for each man, woman, and child in the world to have one tablet per day throughout the year. It might be interesting to see what correlation may exist between "life-style" and the per capita aspirin consumption in different parts of the country and the world where such products are readily available to all.

In spite of the hard sell come-ons that extol the virtues of a particular brand of aspirin or aspirin containing product, the best medical evidence still indicates that—

1. Aspirin is aspirin—all brands must meet federal purity standards, so buy the cheapest brand of U.S.P. aspirin on the market (Naturally the Bayer Company does not agree with this).

2. None of the aspirin formulations is more effective than an equal amount of aspirin alone (Bayer would of course agree with this, but not the manufacturers of Bufferin (aspirin + an aluminum buffering agent), Anacin (aspirin + caffeine), Excedrin (aspirin + acetaminophen + caffeine), Empirin (aspirin +buffers, etc.).

3. In the case of persons who are known to be allergic to aspirin, or if possible allergic reactions are unknown as with small infants, doctors often will prescribe an aspirin substitute such as acetaminophen. Evidence does exist that two aspirin tablets commonly cause the bleeding of 1/2 to 2 mL of blood into the stomach, although healing takes place apparently with usually no after affects. Aspirin has a special anti-inflammatory action that gives relief from the pain and swelling of arthritis, which makes it still the nonprescription drug of choice for this purpose.

4. Aspirin has also very recently been shown to offer protection against some heart attacks and to reduce high blood pressure during pregnancy, although many doctors still prefer to prescribe acetaminophen instead of aspirin to pregnant women.

Wintergreen is a small creeping evergreen shrub common to eastern North America. A fragrant oil can be separated from the leaves of this plant, and in 1843 the chief component of this oil of wintergreen was shown to be a compound chemically classified as an ester called methyl salicylate. Its similarity to salicylic acid is demonstrated by the ease with which salicylic acid is converted into oil of wintergreen in your experiment as noted in the following equation:

| salicylic acid | methanol | methyl salicylate | water |

The boxes indicate that this conversion involves the net replacement of one hydrogen atom in salicylic acid by a methyl group (CH_3) in oil of wintergreen.)

Oil of wintergreen is used in perfumery and as a flavoring agent. And because it has a mild irritating action on the skin which can act as a counterirritant for sore muscles, it also finds use in rubbing liniments. Even if its smell is not familiar to you, the odor should be pleasantly refreshing and a welcome change from many of the smells prevalent in a chemistry laboratory.

It can be added that the pleasant smell is not due to the fact that oil of wintergreen is closely related to salicylic acid, but more to the fact that it is a type of compound classified by organic chemists as an ester. Esters have, somewhere in their structure, carbon and oxygen atoms connected in the fashion . The remaining chemical bonds (hooks in the structure) can be connected to other carbon or hydrogen atoms. Many of our most pleasantly familiar smells are due to esters, notably many "fruity" and flower odors.

The stronger catalyst sulfuric acid is needed to cause the reaction of methanol (methyl or "wood" alcohol) with salicylic acid in this reaction. A relatively large amount of acid is used to keep the low boiling methanol from frothing out of the test tube when it is heating in hot boiling water.

The final addition of sodium bicarbonate neutralizes this acid catalyst with the simultaneous production of considerable bubbling due to the carbon dioxide gas formed.

$$2NaHCO_3 + H_2SO_4 \longrightarrow Na_2SO_4 + 2H_2O + 2CO_2$$

| sodium bicarbonate | sulfuric acid | sodium sulfate | water | carbon dioxide |

Sodium bicarbonate (baking soda) is also the substance often used to neutralize excess acid on the top of car batteries in order to prevent corrosion of the battery terminals.

Procedure

A. *Aspirin*

1. Weigh out 2.0 grams of salicylic acid and place it into a dry six inch test tube. Measure out 2 mL of acetic anhydride into a dry 10 mL graduate and pour this onto your salicylic acid sample. (CAUTION: *Acetic anhydride is flammable and corrosive and has a potent odor. Do not spill this chemical onto your skin.*). Add approximately 0.4 gram of sodium acetate (CH_3COONa) to the test tube and mix well with a solid stirring rod or glass tube that has the business end sealed up.

Pop the 6 inch tube plus contents into a 250 mL beaker half full of boiling water for 10 minutes. Mix the solution periodically during this heating period until the remaining solid has completely dissolved.

2. After heating, pour the contents of the test tube into 30 mL of water contained in a 125 mL Erlenmeyer flask. Swirl and agitate the liquid until the heavy liquid globules of unreacted acetic anhydride which sink to the bottom have completely decomposed and disappeared (under ten minutes). Record your observations. A solid may already have started to crystallize out by this time.

3. Cool the flask contents by swirling in a pan or beaker of ice water. If a precipitate has not already formed, you will have to stopper the flask and shake vigorously as soon as the liquid in the flask starts to turn milky. If you get such a milky liquid, continue agitation and cooling until a solid precipitate has crystallized. Note your observations. If you still have difficulty getting a solid to form, leave the flask in an ice bath and proceed to **Part B**. Solid aspirin should have formed by the time you are finished with **Part B**.

Separate the precipitate by suction filtration using a small Büchner funnel and wash the precipitate twice with 15 mL portions of cold water. (This technique is discussed in Experiment 3, *Recycling Aluminum Chemically*; your lab instructor can also help you with this step.) Don't forget to turn off the suction first before adding each water wash portion. After sucking the precipitate damp dry and when no more liquid drops fall from the Büchner stem, remove and spread the product out to air dry on a smooth piece of paper, or place in an oven for about 10 minutes at 75 °C or under a heat lamp.

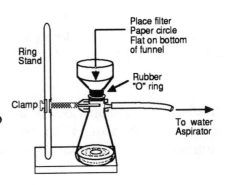

Figure 24.1. *Büchner funnel and filter flask for suction filtration.*

4. When your aspirin is dry, weigh and report the yield (expect 50-70 % yield). Although fairly pure, your aspirin product probably contains a little unreacted salicylic acid. If this experiment required a very pure product, you would have to carry out a recrystallization—a process whereby the crude aspirin is dissolved in a minimum of hot solvent and then the solution is allowed to cool slowly until crystals appear. These crystals would be very pure aspirin. If you wish, taste your product by touching a small bit of powdered aspirin to your tongue.

B. *Oil of Wintergreen (Methyl Salicylate)*

1. Place about one-fourth of a gram (0.25 g) of salicylic acid into a three or four inch test tube. Then add to this test tube 40 drops (2 mL) of methanol (methyl alcohol; CAUTION: *Flammable*). Use a stubby medicine dropper to make this dropwise addition and stir until the solid has dissolved.

Carefully pour a little concentrated sulfuric acid (CAUTION: *Very corrosive*) into a 50 mL beaker—estimate about one-sixteenth of an inch of liquid in the bottom of the beaker. Using the same medicine dropper, carefully add 20 drops of this acid to your sample in the small test tube with periodic stirring using a small solid glass rod. Note your observation. (Your mixture should turn solid.). CAUTION: DO NOT POUR WATER ONTO THE SULFURIC ACID LEFT IN YOUR BEAKER.

DISPOSE OF ANY LEFT OVER ACID IN THE BEAKER BY SLOWLY POURING IT INTO AN APPROPRIATE AND CLEARLY LABELLED WASTE CONTAINER OR BY SLOWLY POURING IT INTO THE SINK WHILE THE WATER IS RUNNING. WASH OUT THE BEAKER AND MEDICINE DROPPER WITH WATER TO REMOVE ANY REMAINING ACID.

Heat the test tube and its contents in a 100 or 150 mL beaker half filled with boiling water. Stir until the tube contents have liquefied and then continue heating for ten minutes.

While waiting, weigh out roughly 4 g of sodium bicarbonate (baking soda; $NaHCO_3$) into a 250 mL beaker, add 50 mL water, and swirl until most of the solid has dissolved.

2. After the 10 minutes total heating time has passed, pour your tube contents quickly (without cooling) into the sodium bicarbonate solution. When the fizzing subsides, stir thoroughly and cautiously smell the beaker contents.

If you wish you may note the taste sensation produced by touching a little of the oil of wintergreen floating on the water surface with your finger and then to the tip of your tongue. Record your observations on the report sheet.

Report Sheet—Experiment 24
Salicylic Acid Derivatives

Date _____   **Section number** _____   **Name** _____

A. Aspirin

1. Appearance of mixture of salicylic acid, sodium acetate and acetic anhydride before heating

2. Observations after pouring contents of heated tube into water

3. Results from cooling the water solution of aspirin in the ice water bath

4. Aspirin yield

    (a) Weight of crude dry aspirin   _____g.

    (b) Percent of maximum possible yield of 2.6 g
    (divide line 4a by 2.6 and multiply by 100)   _____%.

    (c) Appearance and taste (optional) of crude aspirin_____

_____.

B. Oil of Wintergreen

1. Appearance of mixture of salicylic acid, methanol, and sulfuric acid before heating

2. Observations after pouring contents of heated tube into sodium bicarbonate solution

(a) Fizzing _____.

(b) Smell _____.

(c) Oily droplets _____.

(d) Taste (Optional) _____.

C. Conclusions and comments regarding the experiment

Questions—Experiment 24
Salicylic Acid Derivatives

Date _____   Section number _____   Name _____

1. Draw the structure of methyl salicylate and circle just that part of the structure which classifies it as an ESTER. (Hint: see the background section.)

2. How do you know that the oily globules resulting from your oil of wintergreen preparation are not simply unreacted methyl alcohol? (HINT: For help you can look up the solubility (miscibility) in water of methanol (methyl alcohol) in *The Merck Index*.)

3. The following compounds are or were found in common nonprescription analgesic/antipyretic drugs: acetylsalicylic acid (aspirin), caffeine, salicylamide, acetophenetidine (phenacetin), salicylic acid, and acetaminophen. Refer to *The Merck Index* and look up for each of these compounds the MLD (minimum lethal dose) or LD_{50} (lethal dose for 50% of individuals tested) and decide

    (a) Which one of these drugs is the least toxic (to rats, rabbits and hopefully humans)?

    (b) Which one of these drugs is the most toxic?

4. Aspirin tablets also contain binders which serve to hold the tablet together and reduce powdering. Assume that starch is being used for this purpose. Suggest how one might separate the aspirin from the starch. (HINT: Look up the physical properties of aspirin and starch in *The Merck Index*—especially in what liquids each will and won't dissolve).

Think, Speculate, Reflect, and Ponder

5. Baking powder contains sodium bicarbonate plus an acidic salt like sodium acid tartrate or calcium acid phosphate. Suggest how it can "raise" breads and pastries when mixed with water and heated.

6. How do many aspirin manufacturers, whose formula for their aspirin product is exactly the same as everyone else's, make you want to buy their product instead of a competitor's product?

7. Considering the background of this experiment, what statement is the artist trying to make in the sketch* appearing below?

*Sketch reprinted with permission from *Contemporary Chemistry*, E. A. Walters and E. M. Wewerka, Merrill-MacMillan Publishers. Copyright Edward A. Walters.

Experiment

25

The Last Day in the Lab
Glass Etching
Checkout

"The time has come the walrus said
To talk of many things
Of fluorine and glass and paraffin wax
Of chemistry and kings"

Paraphrased from Alice in Wonderland
(with apology to Lewis O. Carroll)

Sample From Home

Bring a small glass object on which to etch a design, name, etc. (Optional)
Glass slides (2" x 3") will be furnished in lab for etching.

Objectives

The ability of hydrofluoric acid to attack glass will be demonstrated by etching a glass object which can then be taken home as a souvenir of the course.

Background

Of all the elements, fluorine and its compounds can be considered as perhaps the most interesting because of the unusual nature of their properties. These properties can range from the highly reactive and toxic elemental fluorine itself, the most reactive nonmetal and the first to react with the "inert" gases, to the insidiously toxic perfluoroisobutylene. On the other hand, the perfluoroethylene polymer called Teflon is exceedingly inert and nontoxic and fluorine plays important physiological roles that are beneficial to life (fluorides for proper bone and especially teeth growth). Also interesting is the fact that some war nerve gases contain fluorine.

| fluorine gas | perfluoro-isobutylene | Sarin (nerve gas) (1 mg is lethal to humans) | Teflon polymer | fluoride Ion |

The distinctive and unusual behavior of fluorine is seen in the group of common halogen acids HF, HCl, HBr, and HI. Although hydrofluoric acid (HF dissolved in water) is the weakest acid, it is uniquely able to attack readily the relatively inert substance glass as well as metals. Very strong bases (lye) are the only other common chemicals able to do this—and they do so only very slowly. Because of this property, hydrofluoric acid cannot be stored in glass containers like almost all other reagents. Originally, it came stored in wax containers, but now plastic bottles are cheaper and safer. Interestingly, pure HF (a gas) can be and is shipped and stored in metal cylinders if bone dry (recall how rusting requires the presence of water also).

"Glass" is largely composed of silicon dioxide which, in the pure state, is known as quartz or "crystal." Dissolving impurities in the quartz both lowers its melting point and prevents it from crystallizing. Thus apart from its relative chemical inertness, glass is really a viscous liquid much like clear Karo syrup. The special physical property that makes glass somewhat special is that room temperature causes it to become so "cold" that it will not detectably flow any more. We might say that "Room temperature is to glass what a cold January morning would be to Karo syrup—it sets up 'like glass'!" Once one realizes that glass is just an extremely viscous clear liquid it is not so hard to understand why it is transparent and can be softened by heating and then formed into different shapes. (It is said that the bottoms of old church window panes are slightly thicker than the top. Can you suggest why?)

When hydrofluoric acid and glass are brought together, the surface is eaten away—etched—due to chemical reactions such as:

$$4HF + SiO_2 \longrightarrow SiF_4(gas) + 2H_2O$$

$$6HF + Na_2SiO_3 \longrightarrow SiF_4(gas) + 3H_2O + 2NaF$$

$$6HF + CaSiO_3 \longrightarrow SiF_4(gas) + 3H_2O + CaF_2$$

| hydrogen fluoride | component in glass | silicon tetrafluoride | water | a fluoride salt |

The gaseous HF easily dissipates, and the sodium and calcium fluorides formed crumble and wash away leaving the pitted, etched glass surface. Frosted and etched glass can be produced commercially using HF vapor, but this experiment will use aqueous hydrofluoric acid (HF dissolved in water). In order to etch only desired areas, the glass object is coated with paraffin which forms an inert barrier between the acid and glass surface. Etching can then only occur where this protective coating is scraped away from the glass surface.

Procedure

CAUTION: *Hydrofluoric acid is very dangerous, and thick rubber gloves are worn when working with it.* Your instructor will place your prepared glass object into the HF bath, take it out after the reaction has proceeded far enough (approximately 30 minutes), and wash it thoroughly with water before you pick it up.

Coat a microscope slide or some small object of your choice with wax by dipping it into a container of hot liquid paraffin. Try dipping one-half in at a time, letting it cool and solidify, and then dipping in the other half. The entire glass surface which will come into contact with the acid must be so coated.

Using a pen, pencil, or any sharp object, write or draw anything you wish onto your object by scraping away all the wax clear down to the glass surface with the sharp object. Because of the glass' transparency, it is generally best to write only on one side. When finished, give the object to your lab instructor to carry out the actual etching process. (So you may feel uninhibited in what you say about the course or whatever, the lab instructor promises not to try to identify handwriting).

After the etching process is complete, do not scrape the wax off into the sink. One way to remove the wax from your finished etched slide or object is to hold it over a paper towel while warming gently with a cool type (absence of hot inner cone) flame from your Bunsen burner. Most of the wax will drip off onto the towel, and you can complete the job by scrubbing off the remaining paraffin in hot water.

You now have a complementary memento of your struggles in this course. The etchings may be colored by rubbing a colored pencil across the marks. As an added bonus, there are no report sheets or answers to questions to be completed for this experiment.